ACIDS AND BASES

RUSSELL S. DRAGO

PROFESSOR OF CHEMISTRY
UNIVERSITY OF ILLINOIS

NICHOLAS A. MATWIYOFF

ASSISTANT PROFESSOR OF CHEMISTRY
PENNSYLVANIA STATE UNIVERSITY

D1133543

D. C. HEATH AND COMPANY
A division of RAYTHEON EDUCATION COMPANY
LEXINGTON, MASSACHUSETTS

LIBRARY OF CONGRESS CATALOG CARD NUMBER 68-12482

Copyright © 1968 by **Raytheon Education Company.**

PRINTED IN THE UNITED STATES OF AMERICA
Printed March 1968

Preface

Modern Lewis acid-base chemistry serves a twofold purpose in the teaching of chemistry:

(1) It provides a model for correlating and predicting a tremendous amount of descriptive chemistry.

(2) Understanding the energetics of Lewis acid-base reactions provides a basis for understanding the trends and exceptions to trends in chemical reactivity.

A common complaint of professors and other chemists is that students do not know enough descriptive inorganic chemistry. Students claim that, in contrast to organic chemistry, where reactions are based on mechanistic models, inorganic chemistry consists of a lot of isolated facts to be memorized. An examination of the section on nonmetals in recent books on inorganic chemistry substantiates the students' claims. Even some widely-used advanced inorganic chemistry texts present the chemistry of the nonmetals in almost encyclopedic fashion. Models and reaction schemes are needed to correlate the tremendous amount of descriptive information and to make predictions possible. Moreover considerations of the energetics of these models must be understood if the student is to appreciate the difficulties in predicting chemical behavior in complex systems.

Chapter 1 of this book is designed to show the nature and scope of the Lewis model and the very wide range of chemical reactions which fit into this scheme of things. After this introduction, the student should have sufficient understanding of the Lewis concept to read descriptive chemistry and incorporate much of it into this scheme, and thus facilitate the retention of descriptive information.

The second and third chapters provide the basis for understanding the energetics of simple chemical reactions. With this background the student can appreciate the limitations of the Lewis model when applied to more complicated reactions. From the studies described in these chapters an appreciation of the effect of electronic structure on chemical reactivity can be gained. Though these effects may not dominate the chemistry in more complex environments (e.g. polar solvents), some appreciation of the magnitude of the energy contribution which they may make can be obtained.

After mastering the information in the first three chapters the student is in a position to understand the complexities of acid-base reactions in water, which is the subject of Chapter 4. The material is presented in such a manner that the reader can readily gain an insight into the reasons for the many exceptions to correlations of structure and reactivity in aqueous systems, a matter commonly neglected in courses in general chemistry. In addition, the close relationships between the phenomena of hydration, hydrolysis, and amphoterism are brought clearly into focus. In advanced undergraduate inorganic courses, the content of Chapter 4 is likely to be followed by a discussion of the Coordination Model for nonaqueous solvents. The material in Chapters 1–3 provide the fundamental background information for understanding the Coordination Model.

The book is written on a level which permits its profitable study by advanced freshman. The topics covered have significant implications in all branches of chemistry.

Russell S. Drago
Nicholas A. Matwiyoff

Contents

Introduction to the Lewis Acid-Base Concept

There have been many definitions offered for the terms *acid* and *base*. Since very early work in this area involved investigations in aqueous solution, the definitions of Arrhenius restricted acids and bases to this medium. Acids were defined as substances which on reaction with water increase the hydronium ion concentration of the solution and bases were defined as substances that on reaction increase the hydroxide ion concentration of the solution.

In reactions that take place in solvents other than water, one finds other species that react much the same as the hydroxide ion does in water. This led Brönsted and Lowry to define an acid as a molecule or ion capable of losing a proton, and a base as a molecule or ion capable of adding a proton. In this context, the reaction of gaseous ammonia, NH_3, with hydrogen chloride, HCl, to produce ammonium chloride, $NH_4^+Cl^-$, is rightly classified as an acid-base reaction.

The next conceptually important step was taken by G. N. Lewis who redefined both the terms "acid" and "base." The Lewis definitions encompass both the Arrhenius and the Brönsted-Lowry definitions. As we shall see, the fundamental interaction is basically the same in the Arrhenius and Brönsted-Lowry acid-base reactions, as it is in all those encompassed by the Lewis definitions. We will first consider the definitions of Lewis acids and bases, and then illustrate the scope and utility of this concept.

Lewis originally defined an acid as an electron-pair acceptor and a base as an electron-pair donor. An acid-base reaction involves the formation of a compound in which there is a sharing of an electron-pair of the base with the acid. A typical Lewis acid-base reaction is represented by

$$(CH_3)_3N : + BF_3 \rightarrow (CH_3)_3NBF_3 \qquad (1-1)$$
$$\text{(base)} \qquad \text{(acid)} \quad \text{(addition compound)}$$

In modern usage a Lewis base is *any substance which has electron density that can be shared with another substance in a chemical reaction*, and a Lewis acid is *any substance capable of accepting electron density from a Lewis base.* If the product of the acid-base reaction is the simple, nonionized combination of the acid and the base it is referred to as an *addition compound* or an *adduct.* In the acid-base interaction more than one electron is involved, and coordination of the acid to the base must occur. This definition does not encompass reactions which involve only the simple transfer of an electron such as the reaction of lithium with chlorine to form free lithium and chloride ions

$$2\,Li + Cl_2 \rightarrow 2\,Li^+ + 2Cl^- \tag{1-2}$$

However, the following reaction in which the chloride ion becomes coordinated to the lithium ion* would be a Lewis acid-base inter-

$$Li^+ + Cl^- \rightarrow Li^+Cl^- \tag{1-3}$$

action for it satisfies the above definition. The reaction represented below in equation (1-4) is not of the Lewis acid-base type for the reactants do not coordinate with each other or with atomic fragments of each other

$$MnO_4{}^{2-} + Fe(CN)_6{}^{-3} \rightleftarrows MnO_4{}^- + Fe(CN)_6{}^{-4} \tag{1-4}$$

One cannot distinguish Lewis acid-base reactions from other reactions solely on the basis of whether or not oxidation or reduction has occurred in the reaction. Redox reactions may either be of the Lewis acid-base or electron transfer type. Equation (1-4) represents a redox reaction in which an adduct is not involved as an intermediate. There are many reactions in which an adduct must form before oxidation-reduction occurs, *e.g.*,

$$Co(NH_3)_5Cl^{2+} + Cr(H_2O)_6{}^{2+}$$
$$\rightarrow [(NH_3)_5Co\text{—}Cl\text{—}Cr(H_2O)_5]^{4+} + H_2O$$

$$H_2O + [(NH_3)_5CoClCr(H_2O)_5]^{4+} + 5\,H_3O^+$$
$$\rightarrow Cr(H_2O)_5Cl^{2+} + Co(H_2O)_6{}^{2+} + 5\,NH_4{}^+ \tag{1-5a}$$

Equation 1-5b (where $\overline{O}|$ refers to an oxygen atom) is interesting.

$$(CH_3)_3N : + \overline{O}| \rightarrow (CH_3)_3N\text{—}\overline{O}| \tag{1-5b}$$

This reaction satisfies all the requirements of the definition of a Lewis acid-base reaction and also involves oxidation and reduction.

---

* Li^+Cl^- is used to designate an ion pair. The chloride is coordinated to lithium.

2

Although in the examples of Lewis acid-base reactions presented in equations 1–1 and 1–5b nonionic addition compounds are the products, this is not a requirement for the reaction type. For example, the following equation represents a reaction in which the base coordinates to an ionic fragment of HCl, the proton, yet is of the Lewis acid-base type.

$$H_3N: + HCl \rightarrow NH_4^+ + Cl^- \tag{1-6}$$

This reaction is referred to as a *displacement reaction*. The stronger base, ammonia, displaces the weaker base, chloride ion, from the Lewis acid, the proton.

If a Lewis base is to form an addition compound, it must have one or more pairs of electrons which can furnish electron density to an acid, *i.e.*, form a bond with it. In order for a substance to be capable of this, two requirements need be satisfied: (1) the electrons in the base must not all be involved in bonding to other atoms in the molecule; (2) the electrons must not be so tightly held by the nucleus that there is little tendency to release electron density to the acid. Methane, CH_4, does not behave as a Lewis base for the first reason, and the noble gases, with four pairs of valence electrons, do not behave as Lewis bases for the second reason. In contrast to argon, sulfide ion, with the same electronic configuration but with two less protons in the nucleus, is a good Lewis base.

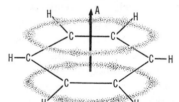

Figure 1-1 Coordination of the π-cloud of Benzene to an Acid, A.

Benzene, C_6H_6, is an example of a base from which electron density associated with more than one atom can be supplied to an acid. This interaction is illustrated in Fig. 1–1 where the π-cloud (consisting of six electrons) is shown to coordinate to a hypothetical acid, A. Some examples of this type bonding will be discussed later.

It is appropriate at this point to amplify the statement that the electrons of the base furnish electron density to the acid. In an adduct, for example $H_3N : BF_3$, it is impossible to determine whether the pair of electrons involved in the acid-base interaction is shared equally or to determine what fractions of the pair should be assigned the boron and nitrogen atoms. The sharing depends upon several factors, including the relative electronegativities of the boron and

3

nitrogen atoms in this compound. We know that nitrogen has less electron density associated with it in the addition compound than in ammonia, and, consequently, we can infer that electron density has been transferred from the base to the acid. It is most certainly incorrect to conclude that a pair of electrons has been transferred to the acid. In Chapter 3, the nature of the bonding between the acid and the base will be discussed. More support for this idea will be presented then.

If a substance is to behave as a Lewis acid in the formation of molecular addition compounds, two requirements must be satisfied: (1) the acidic center must possess a relatively high formal positive charge and have available empty orbitals of low energy, *i.e.*, orbitals with high electron affinities; (2) the coordination number (*i.e.*, the number of atoms which *can* be attached to a particular atom) of the acidic element in the acid must not be satisfied. For example, the electronic configurations of the tin atom in gaseous tin and in tin tetrachloride can be represented by the box diagrams

	5s	5p	5d
Sn	$\uparrow\downarrow$	$\uparrow$ $\uparrow$ $\square$	$\square\square\square\square\square$
Sn (in $SnCl_4$)	$\uparrow\downarrow$	$\uparrow\downarrow$ $\uparrow\downarrow$ $\uparrow\downarrow$	$\square\square\square\square\square$
Sn (in $SnCl_4$)·2$(CH_3)_2O$	$\uparrow\downarrow$	$\uparrow\downarrow$ $\uparrow\downarrow$ $\uparrow\downarrow$	$\uparrow\downarrow$ $\uparrow\downarrow$ $\square\square\square$

Since the tin atom has empty 5d orbitals which are of relatively low energy and since the tin atom in $SnCl_4$ bears a high formal positive charge, $SnCl_4$ is a potential Lewis acid. The addition compound $SnCl_4$·2$(CH_3)_2O$ can be formed by an acid-base reaction between tin tetrachloride and dimethyl ether. In the adduct, the two oxygen atoms of the ether are bonded to the tin atom which now employs two of the *d*-orbitals in bonding; *i.e.*, in the formation of the adduct, electron density has been added to two of the *d*-orbitals of tin.

Since there are five *d*-orbitals, one might question why the compound $SnCl_4$·5$(CH_3)_2O$ does not form. Apparently with these atoms (chlorine) and molecules (ether) attached, the tin atom is "coordinately saturated" when the coordination number is 6. It is found that for most systems the maximum coordination number for tin is six. This maximum coordination number is determined by steric considerations (*i.e.*, the size of the groups attached), the nature of the base, and other factors, all of which will be discussed in Chapter 3. Thus, the molecule SF_6 has empty orbitals of relatively low energy on the sulfur and a sulfur atom of high formal positive charge but does not form addition compounds because the coordination number

4

of sulfur is "satisfied" by the six fluorine atoms. In contrast to $SnCl_4$, $Sn(CH_3)_4$ is a very poor Lewis acid because the tin atom does not have a high formal positive charge. Coordination saturation is achieved when the tin atom bonds only to four methyl groups. Conversely, even though the carbon atom in CF_4 bears a high formal positive charge, carbon tetrafluoride is an extremely poor Lewis acid because the carbon atom does not have available the appropriate orbitals with which to bond to a base.

It should be emphasized that a substance whose coordination number is satisfied can exhibit Lewis acid behavior in certain types of reactions, *e.g.*, consider the carbon atom of CH_3I in the equation

$$C_5H_5N: + CH_3I \rightarrow [C_5H_5N^{\delta+}\text{---}CH_3\text{---}I^{\delta-}] \rightarrow C_5H_5NCH_3^+ + I^-$$

This reaction, like that shown in equation 1–6, is a displacement reaction. The transition state, enclosed in brackets in the above equation, is structurally analogous to an addition compound. However, the acid CH_3I, like CF_4, cannot form stable addition compounds.

The displacement reaction is very common in organic chemistry. The base can be a neutral molecule, as in the example above, or it can be an anion

$$OH^- + CH_3I \rightleftarrows [HO^{\delta-}\text{---}CH_3\text{---}I^{\delta-}] \rightleftarrows CH_3OH + I^- \quad \textbf{(1–7)}$$

$[NH_2^-, C_2H_5O^-, CH_3C\overset{\displaystyle O}{\overset{\|}{-}}O^-, S\text{---}H^-, CN^-, H^-$ can be substituted for OH^- in equation (1–7)]. The extent to which each of the reactions represented above occurs is variable, and the factors which determine this will be discussed later.

There are also other reaction schemes which enable us to include several other common reactions into the Lewis acid-base scheme. As indicated by our definition, hydrogen-bonding interactions, such as that illustrated in equation 1–8, are included as Lewis acid-base interactions.

dimethyl
ether

The proton accepts electron density from the ether oxygen atom to form an addition compound.

Strong bases cause displacement reactions in hydrogen bonding systems in appropriate solvents, *e.g.*

$$H_3N: + H_2O \rightleftharpoons H-\overset{\displaystyle H}{\underset{\displaystyle H}{N}}: ---H-O\underset{\displaystyle H}{\diagdown} \rightleftharpoons NH_4^+ + OH^- \quad (1-9)$$

The ionization of strong and weak acids in water and basic non-aqueous solvents can be formulated similarly

$$HCl_{(g)} + H_2O \rightarrow [H_2\overset{\delta+}{O}---H---\overset{\delta-}{Cl}] \rightarrow H_3O_{(aq)}^+ + Cl_{(aq)}^- \quad (1-10)$$

The addition compound shown in the brackets is a postulated intermediate. The reaction proceeds to completion in dilute solutions. The species H_3O^+, called the hydronium ion, is a simplification of the actual species that exists. The proton is very extensively solvated, and a more nearly correct representation is

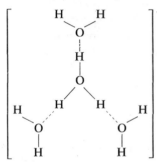

Figure 1–2 Solvation of the Proton in Water.

The terminal hydrogens are also hydrogen bonded to other water molecules, but the interaction is weaker than for those illustrated in Fig. 1–2. For simplicity we shall use the formula H_3O^+ to represent the hydrated proton in this book.

In the case of the weak acid HCN, the CN^- ion is a stronger base toward H^+ than is water, and the ionization reaction occurs only to a very slight extent

$$H_2O + HCN \rightleftharpoons H_2O---HCN \rightleftharpoons H_3O^+ + CN^- \quad (1-11)$$

Thus ionization of protonic solutes ($HClO_4$, CH_3COOH, etc.) in basic solvents can be viewed as a competition for the proton between the anion bonded to the proton in the acid, *i.e.*, *the conjugate base*, and the solvent. In view of this competition, the following very important conclusion can be drawn: *The stronger the acid, the weaker the conjugate base of this acid; and the weaker the acid, the stronger the conjugate base of this acid.* The reverse of reaction (1–11) can be carried out by adding CN^- to a solution of hydrochloric acid

$$H_3O^+ + CN^- \rightarrow HCN + H_2O \qquad (1\text{--}12)$$

The same competition described above (CN$^-$ *vs.* H$_2$O) accounts for the fact that the position of equilibrium lies far to the right.

As mentioned in the discussion of equation (1–10), the dissociation of chloride ion from HCl is complete in dilute aqueous solutions. Similarly, it is found that in dilute aqueous solution, I$^-$ is completely dissociated from HI, Br$^-$ from HBr, NO$_3^-$ from HNO$_3$, and ClO$_4^-$ from HClO$_4$. In every instance the acidic species produced is H$_3$O$^+$. The acidity of all these acids is "leveled" in water to that of H$_3$O$^+$. Since the strongest acid that can exist in water is H$_3$O$^+$, any stronger acid, when dissolved, will react with the water and have its acidity leveled by producing the hydronium ion. In liquid ammonia, the strongest acid that can exist is NH$_4^+$, and the acidity of all stronger acids will be leveled to that of this species by reaction with NH$_3$. In liquid ammonia, even HOAc undergoes complete proton transfer to produce ammonium ion. Since H$_3$O$^+$ is a stronger acid than NH$_4^+$, more highly acidic conditions can be obtained in the solvent water than in ammonia.

The hydrolysis of strongly basic anions, *i.e.*, conjugate bases of weak acids, can be described by a reaction similar to that shown in equation (1–9)

$$CN^- + H_2O \rightleftarrows [N\equiv C \overset{\delta-}{\cdots} H \overset{\delta-}{-} O - H] \rightleftarrows HCN + OH^- \qquad (1\text{--}13)$$

The extent to which this reaction occurs will depend upon the competition between CN$^-$ and OH$^-$ for the proton, *i.e.*, the relative basicities of these anions. With very strongly basic anions, *e.g.*, NH$_2^-$ or H$^-$, reaction with water proceeds to completion

$$NH_2^- + H_2O \rightarrow [H_2N \overset{\delta}{\cdots} H \overset{\delta-}{-} OH] \rightarrow NH_3 + OH^- \qquad (1\text{--}14)$$
$$ \hookrightarrow \text{etc.}$$

This latter reaction is also a manifestation of the *leveling effect* of the solvent. The strongest base that can exist in water is hydroxide ion. Any stronger base will displace hydroxide from the water and abstract the proton. Consequently its basicity will be leveled to that of the hydroxide ion.

The typical neutralization reaction is readily encompassed by the Lewis acid-base concept, *e.g.*, in water

$$H_3O^+ + OH^- \rightarrow 2\,H_2O$$

The proton transfer to the hydroxide ion occurs because this substance is more basic than water. This reaction can be viewed as one in which water is displaced from the hydronium by hydroxide ion. Similarly, the hydrolysis of the ammonium ion involves a proton transfer reaction

$$NH_4^+ + H_2O \rightarrow [H_3 \overset{\delta+}{N} H \overset{\delta+}{\cdots} OH_2] \rightleftarrows NH_3 + H_3O^+$$

7

The hydration of cationic species in water is included in this scheme because of considerations like the solvation of gaseous sodium ion

$$Na_{(g)}^+ + 6H_2O \rightleftarrows Na(OH_2)_6^+{}_{(solv)} \qquad (1-15)$$

The interaction is largely the result of the electrostatic attraction between the negative end of the water molecule and the positively charged sodium ion. Very little electron density is actually donated to the sodium ion, but we shall include this interaction in the Lewis acid-base scheme because it is very difficult to measure the amount of covalency in a bond and, even if we could, setting a minimum covalency in an interaction necessary to classify it as a Lewis acid-base type would be arbitrary.

We have now seen that water can behave as a Lewis acid, *e.g.*, equations (1-9), (1-13) and (1-14) or as a Lewis base, *e.g.*, equations (1-10), (1-11) and (1-15). As a matter of fact, the high degree of association of water via extensive hydrogen bonding illustrates the fact that a given water molecule is simultaneously behaving as a Lewis acid and as a Lewis base.

When the ion dissolved in water is more highly charged and smaller than the sodium ion, hydrolysis reactions can be expected.

$$Al_{(g)}^{3+} + 6H_2O \rightleftarrows Al(H_2O)_6^{3+}{}_{(solv)} \xrightarrow{H_2O} Al(H_2O)_5OH^{2+} + H_3O^+ \quad (1-16)$$

The aluminum ion interacts so strongly with water that in $Al(H_2O)_6{}^{3+}$ a considerable amount of electron density is transferred from the oxygen atoms to the aluminum ion. As a consequence, the hydrogen atoms in the coordinated water molecules become more protonic and proton transfer to solvent water is facilitated, *i.e.*, $Al(H_2O)_5OH^{2+}$ and H_2O compete as bases for the proton. Since this metal ion interacts very strongly with water, further hydrolysis can occur

$$Al(H_2O)_5OH^{2+} + H_2O \rightleftarrows Al(H_2O)_4(OH)_2^+ + H_3O^+ \rightarrow etc. \quad (1-17)$$

As this hydrolysis reaction proceeds in a stepwise manner, the net charge on the cation decreases and it becomes increasingly more difficult to remove protons. However, very strong bases, such as hydroxide ion, can cause

$$Al(H_2O)_4(OH)_2{}^+ + OH^- \rightarrow Al(H_2O)_3(OH)_3 + H_2O \qquad (1-18)$$

$$Al(H_2O)_3(OH)_3 + OH^- \rightarrow Al(OH)_4{}^- + 3\,H_2O \qquad (1-19)$$

The formula $Al(H_2O)_3(OH)_3$ is an idealized representation of the formula for aluminum hydroxide. This is a much more complex material than is suggested by this formula. It contains hydroxyl bridges which join aluminum atoms and it contains indefinite amounts of water; *i.e.*, the following can occur

$$2\,Al(H_2O)_3(OH)_3 \rightleftarrows (HO)_3(H_2O)_2Al(OH)Al(H_2O)_3(OH)_2 + H_2O$$

$$(1\text{--}20)$$

This type of reaction can occur many more times, joining together many aluminum ions into a single molecule. It is also possible for a single aluminum ion to be bonded through hydroxyl bridges to three or more other aluminum ions. Repetition of this process leads to the formation of high molecular weight materials which are called inorganic polymers. Matijevic[1] has shown that the species produced from hydrolysis can be formulated as $Al_8(OH)_{20}^{4+}$. The formula of the insoluble hydroxide is often represented as $Al_2O_3 \cdot xH_2O$. With regard to equation 1–19, it should be emphasized that the coordination number of aluminum in $Al(OH)_4^-$ is four. It should also be pointed out that the reverse reactions of 1–18 and 1–19 can be made to occur by adding strong acids to the products. This results in the protonation of the coordinated hydroxide.

The reactions and considerations discussed above can be extended easily to protonic solvents other than water. Such an extension encompasses solvation, solvolysis, proton transfer, and complexation reactions in these solvents as interactions of the Lewis acid-base type. The extension of these considerations to the general area of non-aqueous solvents has been described in the literature.[2]

To summarize the above discussion, we can correlate a good deal of chemistry *by first considering the Lewis acid or base properties of a large number of substances, then proposing a Lewis acid-base adduct for the interaction of an acid with a base, and then considering subsequent reactions that this acid-base adduct can undergo.* In some systems, the addition compound exists, *e.g.*, $H_3N^{\delta+}\cdots H\overset{\delta-}{-}OH$, or is a hypothetical intermediate and in others it is a transition state or a proposed transition state, *e.g.*, $[C_5H_5N\text{---}\overset{\delta+}{CH_3}\text{---}\overset{\delta-}{Br}]$ or $[\overset{\delta+}{H_2O}\text{---}H\text{---}\overset{\delta-}{Cl}]$. The subsequent reactions which these addition compounds undergo include displacement of an atom or ion, *e.g.*, equations (1–7), (1–9), (1–10), (1–11), (1–12), (1–13), (1–14) or removal of a proton, equations (1–16), (1–17), (1–18), (1–19). By a slight extension or combination of the reactions that many such addition compounds undergo we can include many more reactions into this scheme, *e.g.*

---

[1] E. Matijevic, *J. Colloid. Sci.* **21**, 197 (1966).

[2] R. S. Drago and K. F. Purcell, *The Coordination Model for Non-Aqueous Solvents*, in "Progress in Inorganic Chemistry," Volume 6, edited by F. A. Cotton, Academic Press, 1965.

9

$$AlCl_3 + H_2O \rightarrow [AlCl_3 \cdot H_2O]$$

$$AlCl_3 \cdot H_2O + 5 H_2O \xrightarrow{HCl} Al(H_2O)_6{}^{3+} + 3 Cl^-, \text{ or in base}$$

$$2[AlCl_3 \cdot H_2O] + 3 OH^- \xrightarrow{(x-2)H_2O} Al_2O_3 \cdot xH_2O + 3 Cl^- \qquad (1-21)$$

The displacement of chloride ion by water is similar to the reaction represented in equation (1–10). The removal of protons from the coordinated water is similar to that shown in equations (1–17) and (1–18). In some cases of this sort, not all of the chloride is displaced, either because of the insolubility of an intermediate or because of the decrease in the acidity of the central metal ion, *e.g.*

$$BiCl_3 + (x + 3)H_2O \rightarrow BiOCl \cdot x\, H_2O + 2 H_3O^+ + 2 Cl^- \qquad (1-22)$$

Titanium tetrafluoride reacts with di-*n*-propylamine, $(C_3H_7)_2NH$, but the extent of fluoride ion displacement in this reaction is quite slight.

$$(3/2)x\ TiF_4 + 2x\ (C_3H_7)_2NH$$

$$\rightarrow [(C_3H_7)_2NTiF_3]_x + x(C_3H_7)_2NH_2{}^+ + \frac{x}{2} TiF_6{}^{2-} \qquad (1-23)$$

For this reaction, it has been shown[3] that fluoride ion is displaced first and the proton is then removed to form $(C_3H_7)_2NTiF_3$ if excess propylamine is added to a solution of the acid. There are metal halides, in which the oxidation state of the metal is two or more, that undergo extensive solvolysis in protonic, basic solvents, *e.g.*, H_2O, NH_3, R_2NH, and H_2S

$$TiCl_4 + NH_3 \xrightarrow{(KNH_2)} Ti_3N_4 \cdot x\ NH_3 + NH_4{}^+Cl^- \qquad (1-24)$$

Depending upon conditions, all or some of the chloride ions can be replaced. The extent of chloride ion displacement can be increased if stronger bases are added, *e.g.*, KNH_2 in liquid ammonia or KOH in water. The formula $Ti_3N_4 \cdot x\ NH_3$ represents a complex structure containing NH_2 and NH bridges.

It is now appropriate to present some examples which illustrate the scope of the reactions included by this concept. The reactions shown by the following equations are very similar to the one represented in equation (1–1).

$$(CH_3)_3N + SO_3 \rightleftarrows (CH_3)_3NSO_3 \qquad (1-25)$$

$$(CH_3)_3N + SO_2 \rightleftarrows (CH_3)_3NSO_2 \qquad (1-26)$$

$$2 (CH_3)_2S + CdI_2 \rightleftarrows [(CH_3)_2S]_2CdI_2 \qquad (1-28)$$

---

[3] J. A. Chandler, J. E. Wuller, and R. S. Drago, *Inorg. Chem.* **1**, 65 (1962).

$$2\,H_3N + HgCl_2 \xrightarrow{\text{(NH}_3)_{\text{liq}}} (H_3N)_2HgCl_2 \quad \text{(1–29)}$$

$$2\,F^- + TiF_4 \rightleftarrows TiF_6{}^{2-} \quad \text{(1–30)}$$

$$(CH_3)_2O + \text{[N–N structure]} \rightleftarrows \text{[N–N structure]} \quad \text{(1–31)}$$

$$(PtCl_2)_n + 2n\,(C_2H_5)_3P \rightleftarrows n(C_2H_5)_3P\text{[Pt–Pt bridged structure]}P(C_2H_5)_3 \quad \text{(1–32)}$$

$$(CH_3)_3N + I_2 \rightleftarrows (CH_3)_3\overset{\delta+}{N} : \overset{\delta-}{\underline{I}\!-\!\underline{\overline{I}}} \quad \text{(1–33)}$$

Reaction (1–33) must be carried out in very dilute solutions of hexane, otherwise further reaction occurs according to

$$2\,(CH_3)_3NI_2 \rightleftarrows (CH_3)_3NI^+ + I_3{}^- + (CH_3)_3N \quad \text{(1–34)}$$

The reaction represented by equation (1–34) is a displacement reaction similar to that shown by equation (1–6). The reaction is one in which the base $(CH_3)_3N$ displaces the weaker base I^- from the acid I^+.

$$(CH_3)_3N + I\!-\!I \rightleftarrows (CH_3)_3\overset{\delta+}{N}\!-\!I\!-\!\overset{\delta-}{I} \rightleftarrows (CH_3)_3NI^+ + I^- \quad \text{(1–35)}$$

$$I^- + (CH_3)_3NI_2 \rightleftarrows (CH_3)_3N + I_3{}^- \quad \text{(1–36)}$$

In this system I^- combines with I_2 to form $I_3{}^-$ because of the stability of this latter species. Many bases undergo these reactions (equations 1–33 and 1–36) with iodine but it is not known for certain whether the ionization reaction occurs as indicated above (equation 1–36) when appreciable quantities of the addition compound are formed or whether the reaction occurs according to

$$(CH_3)_3NI_2 + (CH_3)_3N \rightleftarrows [(CH_3)_3N]_2I^+ + I^- \quad \text{(1–37)}$$
$$\hookrightarrow I_3{}^-$$

More research is needed before this question can be answered.

Both of these reaction schemes leading to $I_3{}^-$ would be included as Lewis acid-base displacement reactions. The following represent a similar series of reactions involving acids other than iodine.

$$ICl + 2\,(CH_3)_3N \rightleftarrows [(CH_3)_3N]_2I^+ + ICl_2{}^- \quad \text{(1–38)}$$

$$(FeCl_3)_x + mCH_3C\!\equiv\!N \rightleftarrows \frac{x}{2}Cl_2Fe(N\!\equiv\!C\!-\!CH_3)_m{}^+ + \frac{x}{2}FeCl_4{}^- \quad \text{(1–39)}$$

$$2\,C_5H_5N + N_2O_4 \rightleftarrows (C_5H_5N)_2NO^+ + NO_3{}^- \quad \text{(1–40)}$$

$$2\,PCl_5 + 2\,CH_3CN \rightleftarrows (CH_3CN)_2PCl_4{}^+ + PCl_6{}^- \quad \text{(1–41)}$$

$$O=PCl_3 + C_5H_5N \rightleftarrows C_5H_5NP\overset{O}{\overset{\|}{C}}l_2^+ + Cl^- \tag{1-42}$$

$$Co_2(CO)_8 + C_2H_5OH \rightleftarrows [Co(CO)_4HOC_2H_5]^+ + Co(CO)_4^- \tag{1-43}$$

The products represented in equation (1–40) can be accounted for by

$$C_5H_5\overset{O}{\underset{O}{N-N-NO_2}} + C_5H_5N \rightarrow (C_5H_5N)_2NO_2^+ + NO_2^-$$

$$\rightarrow (C_5H_5N)_2NO^+ + NO_3^- \tag{1-44}$$

Oxidation of nitrite may occur after the initial dissociation or, more likely, the oxygen is transferred as the nitrogen-nitrogen bond is broken in a concerted mechanism.

It should be easy to see the similarity between the systems discussed above and the reactions

$$H_2O + Cl_2 \rightleftarrows [H_2\overset{\delta^+}{O}---Cl---\overset{\delta^-}{C}l] \xrightarrow{H_2O} HOCl + H_3O^+ + Cl^- \tag{1-45}$$

$$2\,POCl_3 + 3\,H_2O \rightarrow 2\,H_3O^+ + 2\,Cl^- + Cl_2\overset{O}{P}O\overset{O}{P}Cl_2$$
$$2\,(HO)_3P=O + 4\,H_3O^+ + 4\,Cl^- \xleftarrow{H_2O} \tag{1-46}$$

$$CH_3\overset{O}{\overset{\|}{C}}Cl + 2\,NH_3 \rightleftarrows CH_3\overset{O}{\overset{\|}{C}}NH_2 + NH_4^+Cl^- \tag{1-47}$$

$$H_3N: + H_2\bar{N}Cl \rightarrow [H_3NNH_2^+Cl^-] \xrightarrow{NH_3} N_2H_4 + NH_4Cl \tag{1-48}$$

The addition compounds formed between diborane and many protonic bases undergo subsequent reactions in which H_2 is eliminated, *e.g.*

$$2\,(CH_3)_2NH + B_2H_6 \rightarrow 2 \begin{bmatrix} & H & & H \\ & \diagdown & & \diagup \\ CH_3 & -N & -B & -H \\ & \diagup & & \diagdown \\ CH_3 & & & H \end{bmatrix}$$

$$\rightarrow 2\,H_2 + 2\,(CH_3)_2N=BH_2 \tag{1-49}$$

Coordination of the nitrogen atom to the boron atom apparently increases the hydridic character (formal negative charge) of the hydrogen on the boron atom and increases the protonic character of the hydrogen on nitrogen. The elimination reaction can *formally* be considered to be the neutralization of a protonic hydrogen by a hydridic one much like the reaction between the hydrogen ion and hydride ion ($H^+ + H^- \rightarrow H_2$).

Many other reactions fit into this scheme if allowance is made for intramolecular rearrangements. For example

$$SO_3 + H_2O \rightleftarrows \left[\begin{array}{c} H \\ \diagdown \\ \diagup \\ H \end{array} O{-}\overset{\displaystyle O}{\underset{\displaystyle O}{\overset{\diagup}{\underset{\diagdown}{S}}}}{-}O \right] \rightarrow H{-}O{-}\overset{\displaystyle O}{\underset{\displaystyle O}{\overset{\diagup}{\underset{\diagdown}{S}}}}{-}OH \qquad (1\text{--}50)$$

Formation of the addition compound reduces the basicity of the water oxygen atom and increases the basicity of the SO_3 oxygen atoms. A simple proton transfer to the more basic oxygen produces the product. The following reaction is similar.

$$CO_2 + H_2O \rightleftarrows [H_2O{-}\overset{\displaystyle O}{\overset{\diagup}{C}}{-}O] \rightleftarrows HO{-}\overset{\displaystyle O}{\overset{\diagup\diagup}{C}}{-}OH \qquad (1\text{--}51)$$

Triethylphosphite, $(C_2H_5O)_3P$, reacts with CH_3I [in a manner similar to the CH_3I reaction represented in equation (1–28)]

$$(C_2H_5O)_3P + CH_3I \rightleftarrows [(C_2H_5O)_3PCH_3{}^+I^-] \qquad (1\text{--}52)$$

The intermediate $[(C_2H_5O)_3PCH_3{}^+I^-]$ undergoes the reaction

$$(C_2H_5O)_3PCH_3{}^+ + I^- \rightarrow C_2H_5I + CH_3 - \overset{\displaystyle O}{\overset{\diagup\diagup}{P}}(OC_2H_5)_2 \qquad (1\text{--}53)$$

By a similar reaction, a very small amount of CH_3I is found to catalyze the rearrangement of $(CH_3O)_3P$ to $CH_3\overset{\displaystyle O}{\overset{\diagup\diagup}{P}}(OCH_3)_2$. Similarly, the hydrolysis of PCl_3 gives $H{-}\overset{\displaystyle O}{\overset{\diagup\diagup}{P}}{-}(OH)_2$ and the solvolysis of PCl_3 in ethanol produces $H\overset{\displaystyle O}{\overset{\diagup\diagup}{P}}{-}(OC_2H_5)_2$.

This approach to the classification of chemical reactions does not always enable one to predict from fundamental principles how a new substance will undergo chemical reactions and what the structures of the products will be. The extension of these concepts to new substances is empirical and requires that experiments be carried out to indicate how model systems behave. Such a study, coupled with structural investigations, will indicate the mode of reaction of an acid or a base. The Lewis acid-base concept can then be employed to generalize, suggest, and predict new reactions. For example, thiosulfuric acid, $H_2S_2O_3$, is unstable in water but can be prepared in nonaqueous solvents by the reaction of HCl and $Na_2S_2O_3$. Similarly, the acidic properties of SO_3 and donor properties of H_2S suggests that the Lewis acid-base reaction of these substances in a nonaqueous solvent should produce $H_2S_2O_3$. This is found to be the case.

It should be emphasized that in much of the above discussion the mechanisms for the reactions were assumed. In most cases we do not have the necessary kinetic data to establish these proposed mechanisms. Many of the proposed intermediates have not been isolated. As more information becomes available we will be able to put these concepts to a real test.

In the next chapter we shall be concerned with evaluating the magnitude of the interaction between an acid and a base. Since this Lewis acid-base interaction is common to all the above reactions, such studies are essential to a clear understanding of a great deal of chemistry.

Suggested Additional Readings

Luder and Zuffanti, *The Electronic Theory of Acids and Bases*, Wiley, New York (1946).

C. VanderWerf, *Acids and Bases*, Reinhold, New York (1961).

L. Audrieth and J. Kleinberg, *Non-Aqueous Solvents*, Wiley, New York (1953).

CHAPTER 2

Quantitative Description of Acid-Base Behavior

INTRODUCTION

In order to have a complete understanding of any body of information it is necessary to put that information on a quantitative basis. In our case, it is important to set up quantitative criteria for the strengths of acids and bases. Once these criteria have been established we shall be in position to search for an explanation of the data. We shall have an understanding of the system only when both of these objectives have been reached. This Chapter will be devoted to developing a quantitative basis for acid-base behavior and Chapters 3 and 4 to interpreting the data that have been reported in the literature. Since so much of chemistry can be classified by the Lewis acid-base concept, the material to be presented here is of considerable importance to all branches of chemistry.

From the examples listed in the previous chapter, it is evident that acid-base reactions can be classified as either base (or acid) displacement reactions (equation 2–1) or adduct formation reactions (equation 2–2)

$$\text{AX} + \text{B} \rightleftarrows \text{AB} + \text{X} \qquad \text{(2-1)}$$
$$\text{(Acid)} \quad \text{(Base)} \rightleftarrows \text{(Acid)} \quad \text{(Base)}$$

or

$$\text{A} + \text{B} \rightarrow \text{AB} \qquad \text{(2-2)}$$

One measure that has been employed to indicate the strength of an acid or base is the extent of the conversion of AX and B to AB and X at equilibrium or, if the reaction is of the type in equation 2–2, the extent of conversion of A and B to AB. Acid or base strength is then reflected in the value of the equilibrium constant, K_D or K_F.

$$K_D = \frac{[AB][X]}{[AX][B]} \qquad (2\text{–}3)$$

or

$$K_F = \frac{[AB]}{[A][B]} \qquad (2\text{–}4)$$

The stronger the original acid or base, the larger is the value of the equilibrium constant. In a quantitative description of acid-base behavior, it is convenient to use equilibrium constants as a measure of the fundamental properties, acidity and basicity. A number of difficulties arise, however.

Because of the nature of the expression for K, it is impossible to specify the acidity of a species without also specifying a base with respect to which the acidity is measured. The dissociation of an acid, HA, in aqueous solutions is often written

$$HA \rightleftarrows H^+ + A^- \qquad (2\text{–}5)$$

It is now commonly accepted, however, that the hydrogen ion exists in solution not as the bare proton H^+, but as the hydronium ion, H_3O^+, which is extensively hydrated by more water molecules. The dissociation reaction in aqueous solution, then, is more correctly represented as the displacement reaction

$$HA + H_2O \rightleftarrows H_3O^+ + A^- \qquad (2\text{–}6)$$

The appropriate equilibrium constant for this displacement reaction is

$$K_D' = \frac{[H_3O^+][A^-]}{[H_2O][HA]} \qquad (2\text{–}7)$$

Because equilibrium constants are usually calculated from data obtained in dilute solutions, the water concentration is practically the same as that for pure water and can be considered a constant because its concentration does not change significantly as the reaction proceeds. A new constant, K_D can be defined as

$$K_D = K_D'[H_2O] = \frac{[H_3O^+][A^-]}{[HA]} \qquad (2\text{–}8)$$

The relative values of K_D can be used to define the relative acidities of a series of acids, HA, in aqueous solution *with respect to the reference base, water*. The larger is the K_D, the greater is the extent of proton transfer to the base water and the stronger is the acid. Conversely, these equilibrium constants can be used to define the relative basicities of a series of anions, A^-, in water *with respect to the reference acid, the hydronium ion*, because the association reaction is the reverse of (2–6)

$$A^- + H_3O^+ \rightleftarrows HA + H_2O$$

The *association constant*, K_{as}, is simply

$$K_{as} = \frac{1}{K_D} \qquad (2\text{--}9)$$

The more basic the anion is, the greater is the extent of proton transfer from H_3O^+ to A^- (*i.e.*, the farther the reaction in equation 2–9 proceeds to the right) and the larger the value of K_{as}. It can be seen from equation 2–9, that the stronger the basicity of the anion A^- (*i.e.*, the larger K_{as}) the weaker the corresponding acid HA is (*i.e.*, the smaller K_D). The base counterpart of an acid (*i.e.*, A^- of HA) is referred to as the *conjugate base*. It should be mentioned that the acidity of an ion like the ammonium ion, NH_4^+, can be compared directly with that of acids of general formula HA by evaluating K_D for the following reaction, which is analogous to that in equation 2–6

$$H_4N^+ + H_2O \rightleftarrows H_3O^+ + NH_3$$

The value of the K_{as} for the reverse reaction permits a comparison of the basicity of ammonia with that of anions, A^-. The following table affords a qualitative comparison of acid-base strengths in water.

Table 2–1

	Acid	*Conjugate Base*	
	$HClO_4$	ClO_4^-	
	HNO_3	NO_3^-	
	HCl	Cl^-	
	H_3O^+	H_2O	
Decreasing acid strength	$HC_2H_3O_2$	$C_2H_3O_2^-$	Increasing base strength
	$Al(H_2O)_3{}^{3+}$	$Al(H_2O)_5OH^{2+}$	
	H_2CO_3	HCO_3^-	
	H_2S	HS^-	
	HCN	CN^-	
	NH_4^+	NH_3	
	HCO_3^-	$CO_3{}^{2-}$	
	H_2O	OH^-	
	NH_3	NH_2^-	

Now the critical question is whether the relative strength of two bases toward the hydronium ion (taken as the relative value of the two association constants) is a reliable measure of the relative strength of the two bases toward another acid, for example a metal ion. There are numerous examples, some of which will be discussed at length in Chapter 3, which illustrate that the relative strengths of acids depend to a remarkable extent upon the choice of the reference base. The following example illustrates this point. The hydroxide ion is a stronger base toward the hydronium ion than is ammonia. The K_{as} values for the reactions illustrated by the following equations are 10^{+14} and $1.8 \times 10^{+9}$, respectively

$$OH^- + H_3O^+ \rightarrow H_2O$$

$$NH_3 + H_3O^+ \rightarrow NH_4^+ + H_2O$$

However, ammonia is a much stronger base than hydroxide ion toward the silver ion. The K_{as} values for the reactions shown by the following equations are approximately 0 and 1.7×10^7, respectively.

$$OH^-_{(aq)} + Ag^+_{(aq)} \rightarrow AgOH_{(aq)}$$

$$2 NH_{3(aq)} + Ag^+_{(aq)} \rightarrow Ag(NH_3)_2^+_{(aq)}$$

Note that all of these reactions are base displacements, since the silver ion, like the proton, is hydrated. As a result, the above criteria for acidity and basicity are limited to the solvent water and the references, H_2O, OH^-, and H_3O^+.

The fact that a variety of solvents is used to study acid-base equilibria introduces another complication in assigning acid or base strength. For example, both $HClO_4$ and HCl ionize completely in dilute aqueous solution; *i.e.*, the reaction in equation 2–6 proceeds to completion. If one were to conclude that the inherent acid strengths of these materials are equal on the basis of this observation, the conclusion would be incorrect. If pure acetic acid is used as the solvent, it is found that $HClO_4$ is more extensively ionized than is HCl. This is another manifestation of the leveling effect discussed in Chapter 1. In some cases, a reversal in acid strength is found when the solvent is changed. An example of the effect of solvent on base strength is shown by the reaction of Cl^- with Co^{2+}. In dilute aqueous solutions, Cl^- is an extremely weak base toward Co^{2+}. However, in acetone solutions, Cl^- behaves as a strong base, forming $CoCl_4^{2-}$ according to the equation

$$Co^{2+} (acetone) + 4Cl^- \rightleftharpoons CoCl_4^{2-} + acetone \qquad (2\text{–}10)$$

The ability of Cl^- to participate in this displacement reaction in acetone but not in dilute aqueous solutions depends not only on the relative basicity of acetone and water but also on the relative abilities of water and acetone to solvate the species involved in the reaction. We shall have more to say about the reasons for these phenomena subsequently. For the present we can conclude that solvent effects have a very pronounced influence on the magnitude of an equilibrium constant.

Finally, a considerable difficulty arises from the temperature dependence of equilibrium constants. To select an extreme example, acetic acid has a larger dissociation constant than diethylacetic acid above 29°C but a smaller dissociation constant below 29°C.

In the next section of this chapter a more useful criterion of acid and base strength will be formulated.

RELATIONSHIP OF K TO OTHER THERMODYNAMIC QUANTITIES

For a given system the equilibrium constant, expressed in appropriate units, is a measure of the maximum amount of work that is made available or the minimum amount of work that must be supplied when the reactants are allowed to equilibrate to form products at constant temperature and pressure. This statement is summarized

$$\Delta G° = -RT \ln K \qquad (2\text{--}11)$$

where T represents the absolute temperature, $\ln K$, the natural logarithm of the equilibrium constant, $\Delta G°$ the maximum or minimum work (usually expressed in calories per mole or kilocalories per mole), and R the ideal gas constant. The quantity* $\Delta G°$ is generally referred to as the *standard free energy change* which occurs in the reaction, and it represents the difference in the standard free energies of the products and the reactants. For *large* values of K, $\Delta G°$ is *negative*; for very *small* values of K, $\Delta G°$ is *positive* (since the natural logarithm of a number less than one is negative). Consequently reactions characterized by large negative free energy changes proceed to an accumulation of large equilibrium concentrations of products (provided that the necessary time is allowed for the system to attain equilibrium). Furthermore, work is available from reactions with negative free energy changes. Conversely, work must be supplied to cause reactions characterized by positive free energy changes to proceed to a large accumulation of products. For example, a large negative free energy change is associated with the reaction of hydrogen with fluorine to produce HF. However, the reaction can be made to go in the reverse direction to produce elemental hydrogen and fluorine by supplying electrical energy. The electrolysis of a molten mixture of HF and KF constitutes the commercial method for producing fluorine.

Before discussing other thermodynamic quantities it is necessary to amplify the statement that ΔG in units of cal. mole^{-1} or k. cal. mole^{-1} represents the differences in free energies of the products and the reactants. The free energy of a species represents the work

---

* One often finds the symbol $\Delta F°$ used in place of the symbol $\Delta G°$, but $\Delta G°$ is preferred.

which is stored in that species. We could concern ourselves with the amount of energy released if the ten electrons and all the nuclear particles separated from each other by an infinite distance were allowed to combine to produce HF. Experimentally this is impossible to do. In actual practice, HF does not lose electrons or nuclear particles in chemical reactions. Consequently, it is convenient to define arbitrarily some other state as our reference energy starting point. This point is referred to as the *reference state* or *standard state*.

A series of different possible standard states that could be selected for HF and their relative energies at room temperature is illustrated in Fig. 2–1. The break in the energy axis indicates that the separated particles are at a very much higher energy state than hydrogen and fluorine atoms. By convention, the free energies of formation of most compounds are reported relative to the lowest energy state of the combining elements. These elements are assigned a free energy of zero at 25°C and at a pressure of 1 atm. Similarly, the standard state of a *pure* compound is the state of the most stable form of the compound at 1 atm. of pressure and 25°C. For example, the standard free energy of formation of HF would be reported relative to H_2 and F_2 gas at one atmosphere pressure; the standard free energy of HF, which is a gas under standard conditions, would correspond to the free energy change in a reaction in which gaseous H_2 and F_2 each at one atmosphere of pressure form HF gas at one atmosphere of pressure.

$$\tfrac{1}{2}H_{2(g)} + \tfrac{1}{2}F_{2(g)} \rightarrow HF_{(g)}$$

Reactions characterized by negative free energy changes often occur with the evolution of heat. The origin of this heat is the change in the internal energy, ΔE, of the system (the system is defined as the reactants and products isolated from their surroundings) plus the work associated with changes in the pressure or the volume of the system*

$$q = \Delta E \pm w \qquad (2-12)$$

---

* The changes which occur in all the systems discussed here are assumed to be *reversible* changes for systems at rest and not in the presence of electromagnetic fields. A reversible process is one which is carried out under equilibrium conditions. For example, the infinitely slow contraction of a balloon is a reversible process, but the sudden contraction of that balloon caused by breaking the balloon is an irreversible process. All natural processes occur spontaneously, *i.e.*, under nonequilibrium conditions and consequently are at least partially irreversible. However, it is always possible to *define* a reversible path for a natural process. The reversible processes are important because only from them can we obtain the maximum work functions which characterize the fundamental properties of the system.

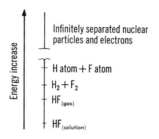

Figure 2–1 Different Possible Standard States for HF.

where q is the heat absorbed or evolved and w is the work done on (+) or by (−) the system as a result of pressure or volume changes. The change in the internal energy is a useful thermodynamic parameter for characterizing chemical systems because it includes, in addition to the changes in kinetic energy, the changes in potential energy due to the changes that occur in states of aggregation, molecular configurations, and chemical nature. Since, however, the heat evolved or absorbed in chemical reactions is often measured at a constant pressure, it is useful to define a new parameter—the change in the *enthalpy* of the system, ΔH. The change in the enthalpy of a system is defined as the heat absorbed or evolved by the system at constant pressure when the only work done on or by the system is that due to volume changes

$$\Delta H = q_\mathrm{p} = \Delta E + P\Delta V \qquad (2\text{–}13)$$

where q_p is the heat absorbed or evolved at constant pressure and $P\,\Delta V$ is the work done due to the volume change, ΔV, at constant pressure, P, each of the terms being expressed in the appropriate units (usually cal. mole^{-1} or k. cal. mole^{-1}). The change in the enthalpy of a system, then, is a measure of the change in the internal energy of that system if allowance is made for volume changes. By convention, when heat is liberated by a system, the sign of the enthalpy change is taken to be negative. Consequently, if a system undergoes a change from a state of high internal energy to a state of low internal energy, the enthalpy change for the process has a negative value. Processes that occur with the liberation of heat are called *exothermic processes* and those that occur with the absorption of heat are called *endothermic processes*.

What is the relationship between the ΔH and ΔG values for chemical reactions? Stating the question in another form: what is the relationship between the tendency for a reaction to occur (measured by the ΔG) and the change in the internal energy associated with the reactants and products of that reaction? All natural processes tend to proceed to the state of minimum internal energy—a system with a high internal energy tends to revert to a state of low internal energy. Hydrogen chloride gas has a high internal energy relative to hydrochloric acid in aqueous solution. Consequently hydrogen chloride gas will dissolve in water to form the hydronium and chloride ions, liberating the excess internal energy largely in the form of heat. The enthalpy change at 25°C for the process

$$HCl_{(g)} \rightleftarrows H^+_{(aqueous)} + Cl^-_{(aqueous)} \qquad (2\text{--}14)$$

is -17.9 k. cal. mole^{-1} (which is merely the difference in the enthalpy of aqueous HCl, -40.0 k. cal. mole^{-1}, and the enthalpy of gaseous HCl, -22.1 k. cal. mole^{-1}, both at $25°$). This *heat of reaction* is liberated to the solution and its surroundings. Based on the ΔH value we should expect this reaction (2–14) to proceed largely to the right. The free energy change is the measure of the tendency of the reaction to occur, and it is -8.6 k. cal. mole^{-1}. From this value of ΔG, which is merely the difference in the free energies of aqueous and gaseous HCl, the equilibrium constant, approximately 2×10^6, can be calculated by means of equation 2–1. Both the ΔG and ΔH values indicate that the reaction proceeds largely to the right. On the other hand for the dissociation of butyric acid

$$CH_3(CH_2)_2CO_2H + H_2O \rightarrow CH_3(CH_2)_2CO_2^- + H_3O^+ \qquad (2\text{--}15)$$

the thermodynamic parameters are $\Delta G° = +6.57$ k. cal. mole^{-1}, $K = 1.5 \times 10^{-5}$, and $\Delta H° = -0.72$ k. cal. mole^{-1}. For this reaction (2–15) the free energy change indicates that the reaction will proceed largely to the *left*. If the enthalpy change is used as a criterion for reaction, the reaction should proceed largely to the *right*. As stated earlier, however, the free energy change is the true measure of the tendency for the reaction to occur, and if butyric acid is dissolved in water, only a very small fraction of it is dissociated. Conversely, if butyrate ions are added to an acidic aqueous solution, they are converted largely to butyric acid molecules, since for this *association* reaction (the reverse of 2–15), $\Delta G° = -6.57$ k. cal. mole^{-1}.

The tendency for natural processes to occur is governed not only by the tendency to minimize the internal energy but also by another condition: to produce a state of maximum probability or maximum disorder. To illustrate, consider two stoppered reservoirs of equal volume at constant temperature and pressure. One reservoir contains ideal gas A and the other ideal gas B. (An ideal gas is defined as one whose internal energy depends only on the temperature.) As long as the two reservoirs are isolated the probability is unity that a pure gas will be found in any sample taken from either reservoir. Now, if the reservoirs are connected and the stopcocks are opened, gas A will diffuse into reservoir B and gas B will diffuse into reservoir A because of the randomness of thermal motion. When sufficient time has been allowed for the diffusion to reach equilibrium, a sample taken from either reservoir should consist of equimolar amounts of A and B. The probability will be extremely small that a macroscopic sample of the gas will consist of either pure A or pure B. The probability will be much less that, at any time, one of the reservoirs will contain only pure A or pure B. Even though there has been no change in internal energy, this mixing has proceeded spontaneously. The driving force has been the attainment of the state of maximum probability or of maximum disorder. Furthermore, to separate the mixture (that is to bring about the state of maximum *order*) would now require the expenditure of work.

Thus, the free energy for a process is determined by a balance between the tendency to minimize the internal energy and to maximize the probability or disorder. This statement can be summarized by

$$\Delta G = \Delta H - T \Delta S \qquad (2\text{--}16)$$

where T is the absolute temperature, and ΔS, called the *change in the entropy*, represents the change in the probability of the state of the system (specifically the thermodynamic probability). For the diffusion process above, the more probable equilibrium configuration is not the pure starting materials A and B but the equimolar mixture. The entropy change associated with mixing, ΔS, has a positive value and the resulting free energy change has a negative value, appropriate to spontaneous processes.

Since the enthalpy change for many reactions is temperature independent, at least over small temperature ranges, the temperature dependence of ΔG and, in turn, K arises largely from the $T \Delta S$ term in equation (2–16). Consequently, to characterize acid-base systems completely it is necessary to evaluate both ΔS and ΔH for acid-base reactions (ΔS is evaluated from ΔG and ΔH using equation 2–16). In the appropriate systems, ΔS will provide information about the "ordering" or "disordering" effects which accompany the formation of addition compounds or the occurrence of displacement reactions.

For example, in Table 2–2 are listed the thermodynamic data for the formation of addition compounds between boron trimethyl, a Lewis acid, and the bases methylamine (CH_3NH_2) and ethylamine ($CH_3CH_2NH_2$), according to

$$(CH_3)_3B_{(gas)} + : NH_2R_{(gas)} \rightarrow (CH_3)_3B : NH_2R_{(gas)} \qquad (2\text{--}17)$$

where R = $-CH_3$ or $-CH_2CH_3$. The enthalpy change for the

23

reaction of ethylamine with boron trimethyl is more negative than that for the reaction of methylamine; this indicates a larger decrease in the internal energy in the reaction of ethylamine than in the reaction with methylamine.

Table 2–2

Thermodynamic Data[a] for the Gas Phase Reaction, 2–17, at 100°C.

R	K	$-\Delta G$	$-\Delta H$	$-\Delta S$
—CH$_3$	28.6	2.47	17.6	40.6
—CH$_2$CH$_3$	14.2	1.97	18.0	43.0

[a] ΔG and ΔH in k. cal. mole $^{-1}$, ΔS in cal. deg. $^{-1}$ mole^{-1} (entropy units, e.u.) and K in units of amospheres^{-1}.

The larger internal energy loss is reflected in a greater strength of the boron-nitrogen bond in the ethylamine addition compound. However, as a consequence of the *relative* entropy changes, the reaction between methylamine and boron trimethyl takes place with a greater decrease in free energy than that between the boron compound and ethylamine. Consequently, the equilibrium constant for the reaction of methylamine is larger. One reasonable interpretation of the *relative* entropy change is that more "ordering" of the reactants takes place in the formation of the ethylamine compound than in the formation of the methylamine compound.

Since the ethyl group is more bulky than the methyl group, more interference would be expected among the substituent groups in the ethylamine adduct than in that of methylamine. The *steric* or *spatial interference* is a repulsive interaction which arises from the tendency of fragments of molecules to avoid the same region of space and forces the ethyl group to adopt, in the addition compound, a restricted number of the many configurations available to it in ethylamine itself. A few of the possible orientations that result when the ethyl group in ethylamine is rotated about the carbon-nitrogen bond are illustrated in Fig. 2–2. In the addition compound, forms similar to (b), in which the methyl group is pointed toward the lone pair of electrons, are not available because the methyl groups of the B(CH$_3$)$_3$ molecule interfere. Because of this steric repulsion, the ethyl group will adopt the configuration of lowest energy—that which does not cause the methyl groups of B(CH$_3$)$_3$ and the methyl group of the amine to interfere with each other. Since the methyl group is smaller than the ethyl group, it is less subject to steric interference. Consequently, the methyl group in the methylamine addition compound should be free to adopt more rotational configurations about the C—N bond than the ethyl group in the ethylamine adduct.

24

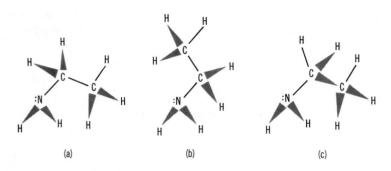

Figure 2-2 A Few of the Possible Orientations of the Ethyl Group in $CH_3CH_2NH_2$. (Recall that the four groups about carbon are tetrahedrally arranged. A similar configuration results from the arrangement of the three substituents and the lone pair of electrons about the nitrogen atom.)

In summary, the ethyl group in this reaction undergoes a change from a rotational state of high probability and disorder to a rotational state of lower probability and disorder. Associated with this change should be a larger *negative* entropy change than the corresponding change for the methylamine adduct.

The entropy changes discussed above account for the main differences between the ethylamine and methylamine reactions but are not the sole source of the *total* entropy changes which occur in these reactions. A very important contribution to the entropy results from the *translational entropy change*, which should be approximately the same for both of the reactions. For both reactants, *two* species are free to undergo translational motion in any direction relative to each other. Since the product is a single species, the amine and the $B(CH_3)_3$ must move together. Thus, the adduct motion is more highly ordered. Associated with this change in the number of particles should be a *negative* ΔS. This is one of the largest factors giving rise to a negative ΔS for these reactions. Although we would be "hard-pressed" to account quantitatively for the separate contributions to the total entropy change in a given reaction, we can often, as in the case above, use the differences among the entropy changes for a series of reactions to draw some tentative conclusions about the nature of the reactions.

ACID OR BASE STRENGTHS AND DONOR OR ACCEPTOR STRENGTHS FROM THE THERMODYNAMIC POINT OF VIEW

In the previous section we have discussed the relationships among K, ΔG, ΔS, and ΔH. The ΔG value for a reaction is a measure of both the net internal energy change and the net entropy change for that reaction. Since it is directly related to the equilibrium constant, it is a measure of the extent to which a reaction will occur. If interest is focused on the equilibrium concentrations of the acids and bases present in a reaction system, then the free energy function is of primary importance. When this property of a series of acids or bases is compared, the terminology *acid strength* or *base strength* will be employed. These terms will be used interchangeably with *acidity* or *basicity*. As previously mentioned, the extent to which a given reversible reaction occurs depends upon the temperature and the solvent. Consequently, any statements about the acidity or basicity have to be qualified with respect to these conditions. On the other hand, if the primary interest is focused on the internal energy changes due to the formation or destruction of bonds and the internal energy changes associated with rearrangements that occur in acid-base reactions, the enthalpy functions are of primary importance. When the enthalpies are measured under conditions where the sole contribution to the enthalpy is from the acid-base reaction (*e.g.*, as when all products and reactants are gaseous), the terms *donor* or *acceptor strengths* will be used to describe the magnitude of the interaction toward a reference compound. It is important to understand these definitions; knowing the exact meanings of the terms is essential to an understanding of the discussions to follow.

THERMODYNAMICS OF ACID-BASE REACTIONS NOT INVOLVING IONS

For the reactions of a series of Lewis acids with a specific reference base, the ratios of the ΔH values for the reactions are taken as the ratios of the acceptor strengths of the acids toward that base (with both the reactants and products referred to a well-defined reference state). Similarly, the relative donor strengths of a series of bases toward a reference Lewis acid are taken as the relative values of ΔH, with both the reactants and products referred to a well-defined reference state.

The reference state chosen for general Lewis acid-base reactions is the gas at very low pressure at a given temperature. In this state the species participating in the reactions can be expected to behave as ideal gases—that is, the internal energy of each species should depend only on the temperature. The choice of this reference state is necessitated by the large enthalpy changes which usually occur in the phase transformations: gas → liquid; gas → solid; or liquid → solid.

For the general reaction we can write

$$A_{(g)} + B_{(l)} \rightarrow AB_{(s)} \tag{2-18}$$

in which A represents the acid, B the base, and AB the adduct. The enthalpy change* is a measure not only of the internal energy change due to the formation of the A—B bond but also of the internal energy changes due to the phase transformations: $B_{(g)} \rightarrow B_{(l)}$ and $AB_{(g)} \rightarrow AB_{(s)}$.

The reaction whose enthalpy change more accurately reflects the internal energy change due to the formation of the A—B bond is the gas phase reaction, represented by

$$A_{(g)} + B_{(g)} \rightarrow AB_{(g)} \tag{2-19}$$

Reactions 2–18 and 2–19 can be related to one another by starting with equation 2–18, writing 2–19 above it and connecting the two with all the necessary energy terms, *e.g.*,

$$
\begin{array}{ccc}
A_{(g)} + B_{(g)} & \xrightarrow{\Delta H_{19}} & AB_{(g)} \\
\uparrow & & \downarrow \\
\| \quad \Delta H_{\text{vap}} & & \Delta H_{\text{cond}} \\
\downarrow & & \downarrow \\
A_{(g)} + B_{(l)} & \xrightarrow{\Delta H_{18}} & AB_{(s)}
\end{array}
$$

where ΔH_{18} and ΔH_{19} refer respectively to the enthalpy changes associated with reactions 2–18 and 2–19, ΔH_{vap} is the heat of vaporization of B and ΔH_{cond} is the heat of condensation of AB (the heat of condensation has the same value as, but a sign opposite to that of, the heat of sublimation). The difference in the enthalpies of $A_{(g)} + B_{(l)}$, and $AB_{(s)}$ must depend only on the difference in the internal energies of the two systems ($AB_{(s)}$ and $A_{(g)} + B_{(l)}$) and not on the path by which enthalpies are obtained. Consequently, ΔH_{18} must be equivalent to ΔH_{vap} plus ΔH_{19} plus ΔH_{cond}.

$$\Delta H_{18} = \Delta H_{\text{vap}} + \Delta H_{19} + \Delta H_{\text{cond}} \tag{2-20}$$

If the numerical values for the quantities in equation (2–20) are inspected, one usually finds that ΔH_{18}, ΔH_{19}, and ΔH_{cond} are negative (representing exothermic processes), and ΔH_{vap} is positive (representing an endothermic process). In some cases ΔH_{vap} and ΔH_{19} are positive, and ΔH_{18} and ΔH_{cond} negative. Under these conditions, the reaction may proceed (*i.e.*, ΔG is negative) in the con-

---

* Throughout this book, the contribution of $P \Delta V$ work to the enthalpy change will be neglected since, for most of the reactions discussed, only the *relative* values of ΔH are of interest and the $P \Delta V$ terms are either small or very nearly constant even for a series of reactions represented by equation (2–18).

31875

densed phase but not in the gas phase (if ΔG for 2–19 is positive). The diagrammatic representation of all the important enthalpy terms in reaction shown by equation 2–18 is referred to as an *enthalpy cycle*. Whenever a reaction in the condensed phase (involving solids, liquids, or solutions) is being considered, all of the important enthalpy terms can be specified by constructing a cycle relating this reaction to the gas phase reaction as done above. The enthalpy terms involved in the above cycle can be illustrated schematically as in Fig. 2–3 where

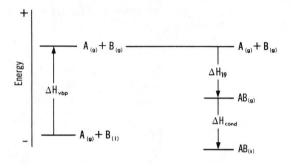

Figure 2–3 Thermodynamic Cycle Relating the Enthalpy Changes for a Reaction in the Gas Phase and in Condensed Phases.

all of the steps in the alternative path (ΔH_{vap}, ΔH_{19}, ΔH_{cond}) are represented. The endothermic processes are listed on the left and the exothermic processes on the right. The difference in the internal energies of the reactants, $A_{(g)} + B_{(l)}$, and the product $AB_{(s)}$ can be seen on this diagram. This difference is the enthalpy change for the reaction of equation 2–18. Since in Figure 2–3 the reactants have a higher internal energy than the products, the enthalpy change for reaction 2–18 is negative.

Most of the data available for acid-base reactions have been obtained from reactions such as that shown in equation 2–18. A calculation of the relative values of ΔH_{19}, upon which the scale of Lewis acid and base strength is based, requires a knowledge of the appropriate enthalpies of vaporization and condensation, as indicated in equation 2–20. Unfortunately these data are often not available. Of course, ΔH_{19} can be calculated directly if the temperature dependence of the equilibrium constant for reaction 2–19 is known (see equations 2–11 and 2–16). Although the enthalpies for some gas-phase reactions have been obtained by this procedure, many acid-base reactions cannot be studied in the gas phase because of experimental limitations (see Chapter 3).

An alternative procedure is available for estimating the enthalpy of the gas phase reaction 2–19. Since most nonionic acids, bases, and addition compounds are soluble in many solvents, the enthalpy change for the reaction depicted in equation 2–21 can be used to calculate ΔH_{19}, if the heats of solution of the reactants and products can either be measured or estimated.

$$A_{(soln)} + B_{(soln)} \rightarrow AB_{(soln)} \tag{2-21}$$

A thermodynamic cycle similar to the one in Fig. 2–3 can easily be constructed. The enthalpy changes for the relevant processes are illustrated in Fig. 2–4. Once again, it is readily seen that the difference

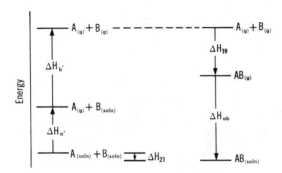

Figure 2–4 Thermodynamic Cycle Relating Enthalpy Changes for a Reaction in Solution.

in the enthalpies of the reactants and products, ΔH_{21}, is negative. It is further seen that

$$\Delta H_{21} = \Delta H_{a'} + \Delta H_{b'} + \Delta H_{19} + \Delta H_{ab} \tag{2-22}$$

where $\Delta H_{a'}$ and $\Delta H_{b'}$ are the enthalpies of desolvation of A and B. These have the same numerical values as, but signs opposite to those of, the heat of solvation of A and B, *i.e.*, the heat liberated per mole of gaseous material dissolved in the solvent. ΔH_{19} is the gas phase enthalpy change associated with the reaction of equation 2–21, and ΔH_{ab} is the heat of solvation of AB. The numerical values corresponding to the enthalpies in Figure 2–4 which are to be substituted in equation 2–22 are positive for $\Delta H_{a'}$ and $\Delta H_{b'}$ and negative for ΔH_{21}, ΔH_{19} and ΔH_{ab}. Equation 2–22 can be rewritten, substituting the more common heats of solvation of A and B (ΔH_a and ΔH_b, respectively) for the heats of desolvation

$$\Delta H_{21} = -\Delta H_a - \Delta H_b + \Delta H_{19} + \Delta H_{ab}.$$

Now when a negative number is substituted for ΔH_a, this term becomes positive. A rearranged form of this latter equation illustrates how the enthalpy change for the reaction in solution must be corrected to give the enthalpy change for the gas phase reaction

$$\Delta H_{19} = \Delta H_{21} - \Delta H_{ab} + \Delta H_a + \Delta H_b$$

It can now be seen that the difference in the heat of solvation of the reactants and products $(\Delta H_a + \Delta H_b - \Delta H_{ab})$ determines the extent to which the "solution enthalpy" and "gas phase enthalpy" will differ.

If the difference in the heats of solvation, $(\Delta H_a + \Delta H_b) - \Delta H_{ab}$, is very small in comparison to ΔH_{21}, then ΔH_{21} will be a good approximation to ΔH_{19}. This condition exists in reactions occurring in the solvent carbon tetrachloride, in which the heat of solution of most gaseous materials at infinite dilution is a *small* negative or positive number. Consequently, there has been much interest in the evaluation of the enthalpies and free energies of acid-base reactions in carbon tetrachloride.

Unfortunately, many acids, bases, and addition compounds are not soluble in carbon tetrachloride, and the enthalpies of adduct formation, ΔH_{21}, must be evaluated in the more polar solvents, such as ethers, alcohols, or water. For the polar solvents, however, the difference in the heats of solvation are usually large and difficult to measure. Consequently, even approximate scales of relative acceptor or donor strengths cannot be constructed from the enthalpies, ΔH_{21}, measured in polar solvents, unless the solvation energies can be determined or estimated empirically. A number of indirect techniques, some of which will be discussed in later chapters, have been devised to accomplish this.

The solvation of acids and bases by polar solvents, although difficult to assess quantitatively, exerts an appreciable effect on the *apparent* strength of acids or bases. Thus, methylamine appears to possess a greater base strength toward BF_3 in the gas phase than in diethyl ether solutions—that is, both the enthalpy and free energy changes associated with adduct formation are larger in the gas phase than in diethyl ether. Since diethyl ether is itself a base, the acid in ether solutions exists not as the "free" BF_3 present in the gas phase, but as the adduct $(C_2H_5)_2O : BF_3$. Consequently the reaction of BF_3 with methylamine in ether solutions is a *displacement reaction*

$$(C_2H_5)_2O : BF_{3(soln)} + \ : NH_2CH_{3(soln)}$$
$$\rightarrow F_3B : NH_2CH_{3(soln)} + (C_2H_5)_2O : _{(soln)} \qquad (2\text{--}23)$$

The enthalpy change in reaction 2–23 incorporates not only the general solvation enthalpies but also the enthalpy of formation of the adduct $(C_2H_5)_2O : BF_3$, which, like most enthalpies of adduct formation, is a large negative number. These enthalpies *reduce* the value of the enthalpy of formation of $F_3B : NH_2CH_3$ in ether solution relative to that in the gas phase, the chosen reference state.

The process of adduct formation in acidic or basic solvents is often referred to as *specific* solvation. The solvation of fully coordinated (coordinately saturated) molecules, *e.g.*, the two BF_3 adducts above, is called *nonspecific solvation*. Nonspecific solvation is due to the dipolar interaction of polar solutes with polar solvents; *specific solvation* is due to adduct formation. Many methods for estimating solvation energies involve a separate determination or calculation of the terms due to specific and nonspecific solvation.

Before proceeding to the special case of acid-base reactions in water, a few more comments concerning the specification of the standard state are in order. No real substance behaves ideally (internal energy depends only on temperature) over all ranges of temperature, pressure, and composition, although many substances deviate only slightly from ideal behavior over limited ranges of these variables. The most important cause for deviations from ideal behavior is the operation of attractive forces among the molecules or ions of a given species. For example, a sample of argon, the atoms of which are spherically symmetrical, will exhibit ideal behavior over a wide range of conditions. The forces between the atoms are weak because they arise from the mutual distortion of "compact" symmetrical electronic levels. The major effect on the gas when the temperature of a sample is raised at constant pressure is to change the volume (that is to do $P \Delta V$ work against an external pressure) and increase the internal energy of the individual argon atoms—a negligible amount of work is lost in overcoming attractive forces between the atoms. On the other hand, a sample of gas composed of dipolar molecules such as HF will deviate markedly from ideal behavior over a wide range of conditions. When the temperature of a sample of HF is raised, not only will there be an increase in the internal energy of the individual HF molecules and work done against an external pressure in increasing the volume, but work must also be done in overcoming the attractive forces among the dipolar HF molecules. This latter work, which can be viewed as $P \Delta V$ work done against an internal pressure arising from the dipolar forces, contributes to the internal energy of the *system*. If the sample of HF is progressively diluted, the dipolar attractive forces decrease because the average distance between the dipolar molecules increases. Consequently, as the dilution increases the sample will approach ideal behavior closely. The internal energy of nonideal systems depends therefore not only upon the temperature but also upon the composition.

31

The necessity for selecting the state of "ideal behavior" as the reference state for Lewis acid-base reactions becomes apparent if two gases composed of molecules with different dipole moments are compared. Since the internal pressures of the two gases are not the same, different amounts of work will be available to increase the internal energies of the *individual molecules* (*not* the *system*) when the temperature of the two gases (both at the same temperature initially) is changed by the same amount. A *smaller internal energy change* will occur for the *individual molecules* of the more polar gas because the more polar gas must perform more work against its *internal* pressure. For the analysis of internal energy and entropy changes in chemical reactions, we should focus our interest on the properties of the *individual* molecules, atoms, or ions participating in the reaction. This interest forces the choice of the state of "ideal behavior" as the reference state for the calculation or measurement of meaningful donor and acceptor strengths. (For the purpose of consistency in reporting and comparing the thermodynamic functions, the reference state chosen is the gas at one atmosphere of pressure and 25°C but in a state where the environment of each gas molecule is the same as if it were at very low pressure.) Our reference state then is not a real state, except for ideal gases, but is a hypothetical state to which real states can be referred by the use of correction factors called *activity coefficients*. The activity coefficient correction will be discussed in connection with equation 2–33.

THERMODYNAMICS OF ACID-BASE REACTIONS IN WATER AND OTHER HIGHLY POLAR SOLVENTS

Acid-base chemistry in slightly polar or nonpolar solvents is largely the chemistry of uncharged molecules. Acid-base chemistry in highly polar solvents, such as water, is predominately the chemistry of ions. The production of ions in acid-base reactions in highly polar solvents is a consequence not only of the large solvent dielectric constants, which are necessary to support the formation of ions, but also of the large base strengths of these solvents. These statements can be clarified by considering the reactions which an acid MX (in which M is the acidic site and X is an element capable of forming the ion X^-) can undergo in a polar basic solvent, B. The reactions are summarized by

$$MX_{(soln)} + B_{(soln)} \rightarrow B_nMX_{(soln)} \tag{2-24}$$

$$B_nMX_{(soln)} + B_{(soln)} \rightarrow B_{n+1}M^+_{(soln)} + X^-_{(soln)} \tag{2-25}$$

Reaction 2–24 represents an adduct formation reaction, the energetics of which have been discussed previously. Reaction 2–25 is similar to the base displacement reaction 2–23 except that, in this case, the base displaced is the anion, X^-. The *enthalpy* terms which are important in determining whether reaction 2–25 will proceed largely to the left or right are: the difference in the donor strengths of B and X^- and the difference in the heats of solvation of the ions and of B_nMX. Consequently, in slightly polar solvents (those capable of only a slight solvation of ions) of small base strength, reaction 2–25 proceeds to the *left*, whereas in highly polar solvents of large base strength the reaction proceeds to the *right*.

The intervention of ions in these reactions in polar solvents introduces a number of complications in the thermodynamic analysis of acid-base reactions. Additional complexities are introduced for solvents such as water, alcohols, and amines (see Chapter 1) which are capable of undergoing dissociation reactions themselves. Obviously, fewer enthalpy and free energy terms are necessary to characterize the reaction of BCl_3 in ether solutions (simple adduct formation) than the reactions of BCl_3 in aqueous solution (equation 2–26)

$$Cl_3B + 6\,H_2O \rightleftharpoons (HO)_3B + 3\,H_3O^+ + 3\,Cl^-$$
$$\uparrow\!\!\xrightarrow{\ H_2O\ } H_3O^+ + B(OH)_4^- \qquad \textbf{(2–26)}$$

The two largest classes of acid-base reactions involving ions which have been studied quantitatively are proton transfer reactions and the reactions of coordination compounds in aqueous solutions. These reactions will be discussed at some length in Chapter 4, but it will be profitable to discuss briefly in this section some aspects of the thermodynamics of proton transfer reactions in water.

As stated in Chapter 1, the dissociation of an acid HA in water, which is a proton transfer reaction, is a displacement of the base A^- by the base water

$$HA + H_2O \rightarrow H_3O^+ + A^- \qquad \textbf{(2–27)}$$

The separate enthalpy terms which contribute to the extent of dissociation at equilibrium can be described with the aid of the thermodynamic cycle shown in Fig. 2–5. It can be seen that the enthalpy change for reaction 2–27 is comprised of the separate contributions from: the heats of solvation of HA (step a), H_2O (step b), H_3O^+ (step c), and A^- (step d); the gas phase heat of association of H^+ and A^- sometimes called the *proton affinity of A^-* (step e); and the proton affinity of water (step f). Since at present it is difficult, if not impossible, to measure some of the separate enthalpy contributions, particularly the proton affinity of A^-, a definition of acid strength based on enthalpies is not very feasible (in special cases, estimates of the separate enthalpy contributions *can* be made by considering additional thermodynamic cycles; for example, see Table 4–2 of Chapter 4). Consequently, the definition of acid and base strengths in water and other highly polar solvents is based on a parameter which is easily measured *directly*—the extent of dissociation. The interpretation of this parameter in terms of internal energy changes (donor and acceptor strengths) is very difficult and will be discussed in Chapter 4.

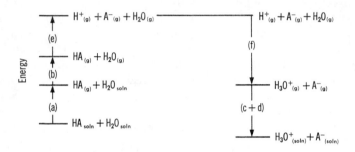

Figure 2–5 Thermodynamic Cycle for the Dissociation of An Acid HA

Since the equilibrium constant for a reaction such as 2–27 is a convenient measure of the extent of dissociation, the relative strengths of a series of acids in water or other highly polar solvents can be taken as the relative values of the dissociation constants, both the reactants and products being referred to the appropriate reference state. Thus the stronger an acid is in water, the larger is its dissociation constant and the larger is the equilibrium concentration of the hydronium ion. Since the general equation for the reaction of a base in water is that represented in either 2–28 or 2–29 below, the stronger a base is, the larger is its dissociation constant and the larger is the equilibrium concentration of *hydroxide ion*.

$$B + HOH \rightarrow BH^+ + OH^- \qquad (2\text{–}28)$$
(for bases such as ammonia and the amines)

$$MOH \rightarrow M^+ + OH^- \qquad (2\text{–}29)$$
(for bases such as TlOH)

Values of the dissociation constants of some representative acids (K_a) and bases (K_b) in dilute solutions in water are listed in Table 2–2 along with the values of the hydronium and hydroxide ion concentrations at equilibrium.

Table 2–3, page 36, shows that values of K, $[H_3O]^+$, and $[OH]^-$ for representative acids and bases span many powers of ten. For this reason it has been found convenient to convert these values to a more manageable scale. For this purpose, the quantities pK, pH, and pOH have been defined.

$$pK = -\log K \qquad\qquad (2–30)$$

$$pH = -\log [H_3O]^+ \qquad\qquad (2–31a)$$

$$pOH = -\log [OH^-] \qquad\qquad (2–31b)$$

The values of these quantities have been listed in Table 2–3. It should be noted that the stronger an acid is, the *smaller* is the value of pK_a and the *smaller* is the value of the pH. A similar statement is true for bases. It is also to be noted that the sum of the pH and pOH values for a given acid or base is 14 at 25°C, because both $[H_3O^+]$ and $[OH^-]$ in solutions of acids and bases in water must also participate in the dissociation equilibrium 2–32 for which the pK value is 14.

$$2\,H_2O \rightleftarrows H_3O^+ + OH^- \qquad\qquad (2–32)$$

Even with this definition of acid and base strength based on free energies of association or dissociation* in water (or other highly polar solvents) there remains at least one difficulty which must be resolved, the choice of the standard state. It has been found convenient to define the reference state of ionic solutes in water or other highly polar solvents in terms of the environment which the solute would have in the limit of an "infinitely" dilute solution. This state is chosen such that the concentration of electrolyte (or other solute) is one molar or one molal but the environment of the electrolyte is

---

* The reader might well question why the definitions of acidity and basicity are not based on the enthalpy changes in the appropriate reactions. There are three important reasons why this has not been done:

(1) It is much less difficult to measure an equilibrium constant precisely at one temperature than it is to obtain a precise value of ΔH from the temperature coefficient of the equilibrium constant. Consequently there are available more values of ΔG for the reactions of a wide variety of acids and bases than there are values of ΔH. However, the recent resurgence of interest in the determination of ΔH values calorimetrically (which in any case are more reliable than those obtained from the temperature coefficient of K) may alleviate this problem in the near future.

(2) For the proton transfer reactions in polar solvents for which both ΔG and ΔH values are available, the ΔG values appear to exhibit a more regular trend with a variation in the structure of the acid and base than do the ΔH values (but see Chapter 4).

(3) From a practical standpoint, the definition of acidity and basicity is a matter of convenience. When acids and bases are used to modify the conditions for a chemical reaction, the interest is focused on the equilibrium concentration of the acid and base.

35

Table 2–3

Dissociation Constants and the Hydroxide and Hydronium Ion Concentrations for Some Representative Acids and Bases in Water at 25°C.[a,b] (Concentration of Solutes, 1M)

Compound	K_a	K_b	pK_a	pK_b	$[H_3O]^+$	$[OH]^-$	pH	pOH
H_2O	10^{-14}	10^{-14}	14	14	10^{-7}	10^{-7}	7	7
ClOH	$10^{-7.5}$	—	7.5	—	$10^{-3.8}$	$10^{-10.2}$	3.8	10.2
CH_3CO_2H	$10^{-4.8}$	—	4.8	—	$10^{-2.4}$	$10^{-11.6}$	2.4	11.6
ClH	10^{+7}	—	-7	—	1	10^{-14}	0	14
NH_3	—	$10^{-4.8}$	—	4.8	$10^{-11.6}$	$10^{-2.4}$	11.6	2.4
$[(H_2O)_5AlOH]^{2+}$	—	$10^{-9.2}$	—	9.2	—	—	—	—

[a] The dissociation constants were calculated assuming the water concentration to be constant; see equations 2–7 and 2–8.

[b] The concentrations of H_3O^+ and OH^- (in mole l.$^{-1}$) were calculated assuming that all species involved in the reactions behave "ideally."

the same as that in the "infinitely dilute" solution. Thus the reference state is a hypothetical state that would characterize a species if it behaved as an ideal solute—that is, a solute in which solute-solute interactions are absent. Actual states can be related to the reference states by the appropriate correction factors, a detailed discussion of which cannot be provided here. The correction factors are applied to the concentrations, expressed in the appropriate units, by

$$a = \gamma c \qquad (2\text{--}33)$$

in which c represents the concentration, a the *activity*, and γ the *activity coefficient* of a particular species. The activity of a species can be visualized as its *thermodynamic concentration*, and the activity coefficient as a factor which must be applied to obtain the correct thermodynamic concentration, the correction being necessary because of the existence of solute-solute attractive or repulsive forces. If the equilibrium constant for a reaction such as that represented by equation 2–21 is to reflect the contribution of the enthalpy and entropy changes characteristic of the *individual species* participating in the reaction, then it must be expressed by equation 2–34 or 2–35 rather than 2–36.

$$K = \frac{a_{AB}}{a_A a_B} \qquad (2\text{--}34)$$

$$K = \frac{c_{AB}}{c_A c_B} \times \frac{\gamma_{AB}}{\gamma_A \gamma_B} \qquad (2\text{--}35)$$

$$K' = \frac{c_{AB}}{c_A c_B} \qquad (2\text{--}36)$$

The equilibrium constants represented in equations 2–34 and 2–35 are often called *thermodynamic equilibrium constants* and that represented in equation 2–36 as a *concentration equilibrium constant*. Thermodynamic data derived from thermodynamic equilibrium constants in which both the products and reactants are in their reference states are differentiated by the superscript: ΔH°, ΔG°, and ΔS°, to represent *standard enthalpy*, *standard free energy*, and *standard entropy* changes, respectively. For the evaluation of trends in acid-base behavior, the standard thermodynamic functions, obviously, will be the more useful and reliable than functions not corrected to the reference states.

The concept of the thermodynamic concentration of a species can be clarified by a consideration of some of the properties of an ionic solute such as magnesium sulfate in water. In an extremely dilute solution (approximately $10^{-4}M$), the average distance between any two ions is quite large and the interionic forces are weak. Consequently, the ions execute their thermal motions (diffusion) independently, and if an electric field is applied across some portion of the solution through a pair of electrodes, the velocity of drift of the magnesium ion toward the cathode is not influenced by the sulfate ion. Neither is the drift velocity of the sulfate ion toward the anode influenced by the magnesium ion. However, if the solution is moderately concentrated (approximately $0.1M$) then the average distance between any two ions is much shorter and the interionic forces are appreciable. The operation of these interionic forces insures that the average Mg^{2+}—SO_4^{2-} distances will be smaller than the Mg^{2+}—Mg^{2+} or the SO_4^{2-}—SO_4^{2-} distances: each ion appears to be surrounded by a diffuse cloud of oppositely charged ions. Because of the attractive forces existing between an ion and its oppositely charged "cloud," the "cloud" retards or exerts a "drag" effect on the diffusion of a given ion. Consequently, if the same electric field is now applied to this more concentrated solution, the average drift velocity of a given ion will appear to have decreased. Alternatively, in so far as the measurement of the number of ions reaching a given electrode in a set period of time is concerned, the *concentration of the ions will appear to be less than .1M*, if it is assumed that the drift velocity of the ions measured in the extremely dilute solution is invariant. It is necessary to correct the actual concentration to the thermodynamic concentration or activity by explicitly taking into account the interionic forces through the use of an empirical coefficient, the activity coefficient.*

The dielectric constant of the solvent is of primary importance in determining the diffuseness of the ion "clouds" or ion atmospheres for a given electrolyte. The dielectric constant of the solvent is a measure of its ability to dissipate partially the ionic forces (the solvent functions much like a dielectric which when placed between the plates of a charged condenser reduces the work necessary to force additional charge onto the plates). If the dielectric constant is made small enough, the interionic forces become large and the ion atmosphere has a tendency to collapse, with the formation of *ion pairs*, M^+---X^-. An ion pair is a species in which there occurs a separation of positive and negative charges by one or more solvent molecules (or another base) and yet which operates as a *unit* in chemical reactions and diffusion processes. The definition given above should not be taken too literally for there has been much interest recently, in the study of "ion pairs" both theoretically and experimentally. The results of these studies will force, at least, subtle changes in our ideas. The formation of ion pairs is an important concept because of the complications it causes in the study of ionic acid-base reactions in concentrated aqueous solution, and especially in solvents having lower dielectric constants than water. In order that the comparisons of acid-base strengths in these solvents be valid, explicit account must be taken not only of ion activities but also of ion pair formation. Since the diffuseness of "ion atmospheres" also depends on the charge of the ions and the ionic concentration (which determines

---

* The reader should bear in mind that this "drag effect" is closely related to the thermodynamics of a reaction such as

$$M^+_{(soln)} + A^-_{(soln)} \rightarrow M^+A^-_{(soln)}$$

Because the nature of the ion clouds surrounding M^+ and A^- will depend on the nature of both these ions and on the concentration of the solution, the thermodynamic data for the reaction will incorporate the enthalpy and free energy changes for the destruction of the ion "clouds" upon the formation of uncharged M^+A^-, unless explicit account is taken of the ion activities. Since it is impossible to measure the activities or activity coefficients of single ions (the measurements must be carried out on cation—anion pairs in electrically neutral solutions), equation 2–33 applied to ionic solutes should be in the form

$$a_{\pm} = \gamma_{\pm}m_{\pm} \tag{2-37}$$

where $a_{\pm}$ is the *mean* activity, $\gamma_{\pm}$ the *mean* activity coefficient, and $m_{\pm}$ is the *mean* concentration (usually *mean* molality) of the cation-anion pair. For a more complete discussion of activities, particularly those of electrolytes, a basic physical chemistry textbook should be consulted.

the average distance between the ions), the effects of ion pair formation are important even in moderately concentrated aqueous solutions of highly charged ions.

Suggestions for Further Reading

The thermodynamics necessary for an appreciation of the quantitative aspects of acid-base reactions have been presented in condensed form in Chapter 2. A more explicit and extensive discussion is presented in references 1 and 2 below, which have been designed for the beginning student, and in references 3 and 4 which are more advanced texts. The relationship between the molecular properties of a system and the thermodynamic functions which characterize the bulk properties of a system is introduced at an elementary level in references 1, 2, and 3 and at a more advanced level in references 4 and 5. The reader is directed especially to the discussions in reference 5 of the statistical basis of entropy and the interpretation of the enthalpy change as an internal energy change. A discussion of standard states (or reference states) and activity coefficients is presented with clarity in references 4 and 6.

1. Mahan, B. H., *Elementary Chemical Thermodynamics*, New York, W. A. Benjamin, 1963.

2. Nash, L. K., *Elements of Chemical Thermodynamics*, Reading, Mass., Addison-Wesley, 1962.

3. Harvey, K. B. and G. B. Porter, *Introduction to Physical Inorganic Chemistry*, Reading, Mass., Addison-Wesley, 1963, Chap. 8.

4. Moore, W. J., *Physical Chemistry*, Prentice-Hall, Englewood Cliffs, N.J., 1962, Chapters 2, 3, 6, 9.

5. Leffler, J. E. and E. Grunwald, *Rates and Equilibria of Organic Reactions*, New York, Wiley and Sons, 1963, Chapters 1–3.

6. Lewis, G. N. and M. Randall (revised by K. Pitzer and L. Brewer), *Thermodynamics*, McGraw Hill Inc., New York 1961, Chapters 20 and 22.

CHAPTER **3**

As mentioned in the previous chapter, the criterion that will be employed to measure the magnitude of the interaction between an acid and a base is the enthalpy of formation* of the adduct, measured under conditions where all species are gaseous or weakly solvated in a poorly solvating solvent. In this chapter we shall be concerned with justifying the selection of data obtained only in the above mentioned media, and with the interpretation of results reported in the literature that have been obtained under these conditions.

ENTHALPY MEASUREMENTS BY THE GAS-PHASE TECHNIQUE

If one considers the stoichiometry of the general reaction for the formation of a 1 : 1 adduct,

$$B_{(g)} + A_{(g)} \rightleftarrows BA_{(g)} \tag{3-1}$$

it is apparent that one mole of BA will be formed for each mole of B and each mole of A that is consumed. If each of these substances behaves as an ideal gas, then the total number of moles present per unit volume in a closed system is directly related to the pressure of that system. Thus, in a system initially containing the same concentrations of A and B, if A and B are completely converted to BA, the pressure of the system is decreased to one-half of the original pressure. If A and B are only partially converted to the adduct, AB, at equilibrium, the decrease in the initial pressure is proportional to the amount of AB formed.

The relationships among the total pressure at equilibrium P, the pressure due to the presence of AB at equilibrium P_{AB} (usually called

---

* For students who have had a year of physical chemistry it is recommended that Chapters 1 to 3 of Rates and Equilibria of Organic Reactions by Leffler and Grunwald (Wiley, 1963) be read for an appreciation of the problems involved in selecting a criterion to measure acid-base interactions.

the *partial pressure* of AB), and the initial pressure $P_A{}^0 + P_B{}^0$, can be readily deduced from the ideal gas law

$$PV = nRT \tag{3-2}$$

where P represents the pressure, V the volume, n the number of moles of the ideal gas, R is the ideal gas constant, and T the absolute temperature. Since we have assumed "ideal gas behavior," we can relate the concentration of each of the gases to the partial pressure which it exerts at equilibrium. For A and B, the number of moles of each, $n_A{}^0$ and $n_B{}^0$, present per unit volume *initially* is given by

$$[A] = \left[\frac{n_A{}^0}{V}\right] = \frac{P_A{}^0}{RT} \tag{3-3a}$$

and

$$[B] = \left[\frac{n_B{}^0}{V}\right] = \frac{P_B{}^0}{RT} \tag{3-3b}$$

The concentration of AB at equilibrium, n_{AB}/V, is related to the partial pressure of AB in a similar manner

$$[AB] = \left[\frac{n_{AB}}{V}\right] = \frac{P_{AB}}{RT} \tag{3-4}$$

From the stoichiometry of the reaction, the concentrations of A and B present *at equilibrium*, n_A/V and n_B/V respectively, can be calculated readily

$$\left[\frac{n_A}{V}\right] = \left[\frac{n_A{}^0}{V}\right] - \left[\frac{n_{AB}}{V}\right] \tag{3-5a}$$

$$\left[\frac{n_B}{V}\right] = \left[\frac{n_B{}^0}{V}\right] - \left[\frac{n_{AB}}{V}\right] \tag{3-5b}$$

These concentrations in turn can be related to the relevant partial pressures (which are the measurable quantities) because the total number of moles present in the system at equilibrium will be given by

$$V\left[\frac{n_{AB}}{V} + \frac{n_A}{V} + \frac{n_B}{V}\right] = V\left[\frac{n_A{}^0}{V} + \frac{n_B{}^0}{V} - \frac{n_{AB}}{V}\right] \tag{3-6}$$

Accordingly, the total pressure of the system at equilibrium, P, is obtained from the ideal gas law

$$[n_A{}^0 + n_B{}^0 - n_{AB}] = [P_A{}^0 + P_B{}^0 - P_{AB}]\left[\frac{V}{RT}\right] \tag{3-7}$$

where P is given by the sum of the partial pressures

$$P = P_A + P_B + P_{AB} = P_A{}^0 + P_B{}^0 - P_{AB} \tag{3-8a}$$

The equilibrium constant, K_c, for reaction (3–1) can then be expressed in terms of the concentrations

$$K_c = \frac{[AB]}{[A][B]} = \frac{[P_A{}^0 + P_B{}^0 - P]RT}{[P - P_A{}^0][P - P_B{}^0]} \tag{3–8b}$$

Although the equilibrium constant, K_c, is expressed in terms of measurable quantities (the pressures), it is convenient to eliminate the factor RT (although it is a constant at a given temperature). Accordingly, the equilibrium constant for the reaction (3–1) is usually expressed in terms of partial pressures

$$K_p = \frac{P_{AB}}{[P_A][P_B]} = \frac{[P_A{}^0 + P_B{}^0 - P]}{[P - P_A{}^0][P - P_B{}^0]} \tag{3–9}$$

the constant factor, RT, being "absorbed" in the equilibrium constant, K_p. By means of a development similar to that given above, it can be shown that K_p is related to K_c for any reaction in which the difference in the number of moles of the products and the number of moles of the reactants is Δn by the equation

$$K_p = K_c(RT)^{\Delta n} \tag{3–10}$$

where K_p has the units (atmospheres)^{exp}; and K_c the units (moles liter^{-1})^{exp}; and R is the gas constant expressed in liter-atmospheres deg^{-1}, mole^{-1}. The value of the exponent, exp., is fixed by the stoichiometry of the reaction.

The measurements are carried out at very low pressures in a vacuum line in order that the gaseous species behave ideally.[1] For example, a known weight of A alone can be transferred quantitatively to the section of the vacuum line which is to serve as the reaction zone, and its pressure, $P_A{}^0$, can be measured with a manometer. After A has been quantitatively transferred to another section of the vacuum line, a known weight of B can be transferred into the reaction zone and its pressure, $P_B{}^0$, measured. If A is then retransferred (quantitatively) into the reaction zone and allowed to equilibrate with B, the total pressure of the mixture at equilibrium, P, can be measured with the manometer. The equilibrium constant, K_p, can then be calculated using equation 3–9. The ΔG^0 value is obtained from K_p with equation 2–11.

The manometer used to measure the pressure of the system is kept at a fixed temperature by means of a thermostat, and K can be evaluated at several temperatures. The following relationship be-

[1] (a) D. E. McLaughlin and M. Tamres, *J. Am. Chem. Soc.*, **82**, 5618 (1960) and (b) L. J. Sacks, Ph.D. Thesis, University of Illinois (1964), available from University Microfilms, Ann Arbor, Michigan.

tween the enthalpy and the temperature dependence of K has been derived

$$\log K_c = -\Delta H^0/2.3RT + C \qquad (3-11)$$

If $\log K_c$ is plotted against $1/T$ (with T in degrees, Kelvin), as has been done in Fig. 3–1, a straight line should result, the slope of which will be $-\Delta H^0/2.3\ R$ or $-\Delta H^0/4.6$ (R, the gas constant is 1.997 when the units for ΔH are calories). If ΔG^0 and ΔH^0 have been determined by the procedures just described, ΔS^0 is readily calculated using equation 2–16.

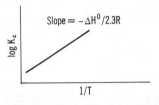

Figure 3–1 Plot of Equation 3–11 for a Hypothetical System

INTERPRETATION OF GAS PHASE ENTHALPIES

A complete enthalpy cycle for the general reaction between an acid and a base in the condensed phase (solid or liquid) to produce an adduct in the condensed phase is illustrated in Fig. 3–2. Step I represents the enthalpy change which occurs in the gas-phase reaction, and II represents that for the reaction of the solid reactants to produce solid products. As mentioned in the previous chapter, if the enthalpy

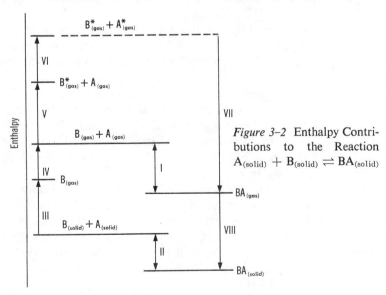

Figure 3–2 Enthalpy Contributions to the Reaction $A_{(solid)} + B_{(solid)} \rightleftharpoons BA_{(solid)}$

change for the following process were measured

$$BA_{(s)} \rightleftarrows B_{(g)} + A_{(g)} \tag{3-12}$$

contributions from step I and the heat of sublimation of $BA_{(s)}$ (VIII) would be included. Measurements of this sort are very common for many solid addition compounds, when heated, sublime and dissociate in one step. Usually it is impossible on the basis of such data to obtain donor or acceptor strengths because the enthalpy change accompanying step VIII cannot be evaluated. Unfortunately, such data frequently are interpreted in terms of donor and acceptor strengths because it is assumed that if two addition compounds are similar structurally, step VIII should be similar for both. Many investigators using this logic have attributed differences of two to five k. cal. mole^{-1} in the total enthalpy change measured for Reaction (3–12) to step I, Fig. 3–2. There is little experimental data available on addition compounds to test the constancy of ΔH in step VIII for "similar" compounds. Moreover, when one considers that two liquids as similar in molecular weight and dipole moment, μ, as $(C_2H_5)_2O$ (MW = 74, μ = 1.3 D) and pyridine (MW = 79, μ = 2.3 D) have heats of vaporization that differ by 2.3 k. cal. mole^{-1}, such an assumption involving solids appears risky. For this reason, data obtained from reactions like that in equation (3–12) will not be treated here, and the reader is cautioned against accepting the conclusions about donor or acceptor strengths drawn from such studies.

It can be seen from Fig. 3–2, that for a gas phase reaction, step I is the net of steps V, VI, and VII. Step V represents the energy necessary to rearrange the base and step VI that to rearrange the acid. By rearrangement energy we mean that energy necessary to put the acid or the base into a geometrical configuration similar to that in the addition compound. For example, BF_3 is planar in the free acid, but the addition compound, $F_3B : NH_3$, is tetrahedral. The energy of rearrangement (step VI) would be that energy needed to convert the planar BF_3 into a regular tetrahedral configuration. Step V is a similar step for the base.

In the experiments to be discussed, the acid studied is held constant in a series of experiments and the base varied or *vice versa*. The experimentally measured quantity is the enthalpy for step I. Steps V, VI, and VII cannot be measured directly but must be estimated from structural information and chemical intuition. Thus, the enthalpy change corresponding to step I is interpreted in terms of the estimates for steps V, VI, and VII.

Some idea of the method used for the estimation of these latter energies can be obtained by considering the rearrangement steps for the acid and base in more detail. The rearrangement steps, V and VI, can perhaps be explained best by invoking the overlap criterion of bond strength. The process of covalent bond formation between two atoms such as boron and fluorine can be considered to involve the overlap of an appropriate orbital of one atom with that of another to form a bonding orbital in such a way that a localized increase of electron density occurs between the bonded atoms. In general, it is true that the greater the increase of electron density in the bonding region, the greater the bond strength. It is also generally true that the more the atomic orbitals contributing to the bonding orbital overlap (that is, occupy the same region of space) the greater the strength of the resulting bond. Consequently, it is expected that the atomic orbitals which contribute to the B—F bond will be those which result in the maximum overlap or the maximum increase of electron density between the atoms.

In the formation of H_3NBF_3 from BF_3 and NH_3, the hybridization of boron changes from sp^2 to nearly sp^3. Changes which are smaller in magnitude also occur in the valence state of nitrogen. This change of hybridization must not be viewed as a *mechanism* for "preparing an element for bonding." The point is that changes of this sort occur sometime during adduct formation and this scheme provides a convenient procedure for bookkeeping of energy contributions. In our scheme (Fig. 3–2), this energy, which provides a large contribution* to the enthalpies for steps V and VI, can be "expended" because the *net* orbital overlap in the bonding region is improved, and the steric repulsions among the bonded groups are decreased if hybridized orbitals are used. That is, incorporation of hybridization changes into the bonding scheme "requires" energy but results in an increase in the heat released in step VII.

It is advantageous to consider step VII in more detail. In order to appreciate this energy term we must first concern ourselves with the nature of the bonding between the donor and acceptor because the stronger the bond, the more heat will be released in the formation of the adduct. Since most of the systems for which gas phase (or equivalent) enthalpies are available are addition compounds of non-ionic acids and bases, the discussion will be restricted to these materials.

---

* Other contributions include changes in the repulsion among the bonded groups and the loss of pi-bonding energy in BF_3 due to the overlap of the lone pair fluorine electrons with the empty p_z orbital of boron.

The acid-base bond in the ground state of an addition compound can be represented by the wave function ψ^0. The ground state wave function can be formulated from electrostatic, ψ_{el}, and covalent, ψ_{cov}, contributions. This information can be conveyed by the symbolism*

$$\psi^0 = a\psi_{el} + b\psi_{cov} \qquad (3\text{--}13)$$

where a and b are coefficients whose magnitudes indicate the relative importance of these two terms in describing the ground state of the particular addition compound being described.

For our purposes it will be advantageous to define ψ_{el} and ψ_{cov} in the following way. The covalent interaction is the typical covalent bonding interaction resulting in this case from overlap of the filled base orbital and the empty acid orbital. Electron density is transferred from the base to the acid by this interaction. This covalent interaction is often represented in the literature by the symbol $\psi_{B^+A^-}$. It should be emphasized that this symbol does not indicate an ionic interaction. The electrostatic term involves (often as the main contribution) the dipole-dipole interaction of the rearranged acid and the rearranged base at their equilibrium positions and distance in the addition compound. Unfortunately, dipole moments of the free acid and base cannot be used to calculate or predict the magnitude of the electrostatic interaction. For example, BF_3 has no dipole moment but BF_3 as part of a molecule in the rearranged state would have an appreciable moment. The interaction of the dipole moments in activated BF_3 and ammonia is illustrated in Fig. 3–3. The more covalency there is in the interaction, the more

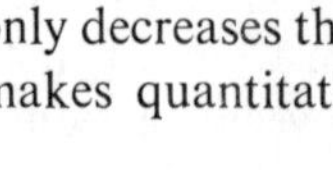

$$F_3B\text{---}NH_3$$

Figure 3–3 Interaction of Acid-Base Dipoles in the Adduct $F_3B\,NH_3$

electron density is transferred from the base to the acid. Since the negative end of the base dipole interacts with the positive end of the acid dipole, this effect not only decreases the electrostatic contribution to the bonding but also makes quantitative estimates of that contribution difficult.

The magnitude of the covalent term is also impossible to evaluate quantitatively. Two qualitative considerations can be used to estimate the covalency expected in an adduct. (1) As discussed previously,

---

* This description of the bonding has been selected because of its simplicity in leading to a physical model. The molecular orbital description is more involved and more exact but leads to essentially the same electron distribution for the bonding pair of electrons. See S. P. McGlynn, *Chem. Revs.*, **58**, 1113 (1958), for a more advanced discussion of the bonding.

increasing the orbital overlap increases the covalency and strength of a bond. (2) If the energy of the two orbitals involved in bonding are similar, the interaction will be greater and the bond stronger than in cases which the energies are dissimilar. Since the lone pair orbitals of the base are usually lower in energy than the empty orbitals on the acid (*i.e.*, the ionization potential of an electron in the donor orbital of the base is greater than that of an electron in the acceptor orbital of the acid), decreasing the ionization potential of the base and increasing the electron affinity of the acid generally leads to an increase in the magnitude of the acid-base interaction, *i.e.*, the enthalpy of adduct formation.

Some experimental gas phase data which can be interpreted by employing these considerations are contained in Table 3–1. The ability of the groups attached to boron and nitrogen to withdraw electron density increases in the order $CH_3 < H < F$.

Table 3–1

Gas Phase Thermodynamic Data[a] for the Formation of Adducts between Some Amines and Boron Compounds at 100°C.

Adduct	$-\Delta G^0$ k. cal. mole^{-1}	$-\Delta H^0$ k. cal. mole^{-1}	$-\Delta S^0$ (e.u.)[b]
$(CH_3)_3NB(CH_3)_3$	0.56	17.62	45.7
$(CH_3)_3NBF(CH_3)_2$	1.2	18.3	45.9
$(CH_3)_3NBF_2CH_3$	5.6	23.1	47.0
$(CH_3)_3NBF_3$	Too highly associated to study		
$(CH_3)_2NHB(CH_3)_3$	2.89	19.26	43.6
$(CH_3)NH_2B(CH_3)_3$	2.46	17.64	40.6
$H_3NB(CH_3)_3$	−1.13	13.7	39.9

[a] The data reported refer to the process $BX_{3(g)} + R_3N_{(g)} \rightleftarrows X_3BNR_{3(g)}$ where X and R represent the groups on boron and nitrogen respectively.

[b] e.u. refers to entropy units; *i.e.*, cal deg^{-1} mole^{-1}.

The *inductive effect* (electron release to the bonded atom) of these groups is said to decrease in the order: $CH_3 > H > F$. As CH_3 groups on the boron are substituted by the more electronegative fluorine atoms, the boron becomes more acidic and the enthalpy of formation of the adduct increases in the order $(CH_3)_3NB(CH_3)_3 < (CH_3)_3NBF(CH_3)_2 < (CH_3)_3NBF_2(CH_3)_2 < (CH_3)_3NBF_3$. Similarly, if the hydrogen atom on the nitrogen atom is replaced by the less electronegative methyl group, the donor strength of the nitrogen increases. The explanation we invoke for these trends attributes the increased negative enthalpy in the series to step VII of Fig. 3–2.

Although there may be minor differences in steps V and VI, we do not concern ourselves with these because no effect corresponding to these steps is known in the compounds discussed above that can account for the measured enthalpies.

In terms of the prior discussion, the acid orbital is higher in energy than the base orbital (*i.e.*, the empty orbital in $CH_3NH_2^{2+}$ is more electronegative than the one in BF_3). If electron donating groups are added to nitrogen, the nitrogen becomes less electronegative, the difference in the energies of the donor and acceptor orbitals decreases, and the adduct bond strength increases. If fluorine atoms on boron are replaced by methyl groups, the compound becomes a poorer acid because the boron atom becomes even less electronegative. Consequently the energy of its empty orbital increases (driving the energies of the nitrogen and boron orbitals further apart) and the contribution to the bonding from covalency decreases.

Note that the series of increasing enthalpies of formation manifested by the adducts is $H_3NB(CH_3)_3 < CH_3NH_2B(CH_3)_3 < (CH_3)_2NHB(CH_3)_3$. It is interesting that the enthalpies of formation of the adduct $(CH_3)_3NB(CH_3)_3$ is less than that of $(CH_3)_2NHB(CH_3)_3$. The decreased interaction in $(CH_3)_3NB(CH_3)_3$ has been attributed to a *steric effect*[2] commonly called *steric strain*. The CH_3 groups on boron and nitrogen repel one another in the region indicated by the shading in Figure 3–4. Since this prevents

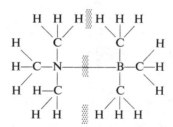

Figure 3–4 F-Strain in the $(CH_3)_3BN(CH_3)_3$ Adduct

the nitrogen and boron from approaching as closely as is required for good overlap, the boron-nitrogen bond is weaker than if good overlap were possible and strain is said to exist. Here the decreased donor strength of $N(CH_3)_3$ toward $(CH_3)_3B$ is attributed to a change in step VII. Since this strain is occurring at the front ends of the molecules (defined as the ends which coordinate), it has been referred

---

[2] H. C. Brown, *J. Chem. Soc.*, 1956, 1248; H. C. Brown and S. Kujishi, *J. Am. Chem. Soc.*, **70**, 2878 (1948).

to as *front strain* or *F-strain*. One could argue that if the methyl groups were moved back, *i.e.*, if the C—N—C or C—B—C angle were decreased, front strain would disappear. However, methyl groups on the back end of the nitrogen or boron would start repelling other methyl groups on the same atom. This effect is referred to as *back strain* or *B-strain*. This argument would attribute the decrease in gas phase heat (*i.e.*, step 1) to an increase in base energy of rearrangement (step V) and an increase in acid energy of rearrangement (step VI). The energy necessary to rearrange the free acid and the base to the adduct configuration is large because of B-strain. Both effects are probably present in this adduct but the relative importance of each has not been demonstrated.

The existence of strain in $(CH_3)_3BN(CH_3)_3$ can be demonstrated indirectly. If one sums the tabulated values for the C—C and C—H bond energies, it is possible to obtain calculated values for the heats of formation of a large number of hydrocarbons; these are found to agree closely with measured values. If this is done for $(CH_3)_3C—C(CH_3)_3$, the heat of formation obtained is 7.8 k. cal. mole^{-1} more positive than that experimentally measured. This is attributed to the existence in this molecule of steric strain which lowers the C—C bond energy below the value expected. Since the C—C and B—N bond distances are similar, it is believed that approximately the same amount of strain energy exists in $(CH_3)_3BN(CH_3)_3$ as in the analogous hydrocarbon.

One additional type of strain should be mentioned. The enthalpy

of formation of the $B(CH_3)_3$ adduct with ethyleneimine,

$$\begin{array}{c} CH_2 \\ | \quad \diagdown \\ \quad \quad N—H, \\ | \quad \diagup \\ CH_2 \end{array}$$

is -17.6 k. cal. mole^{-1}. This is to be contrasted with the enthalpy of formation of the $(CH_3)_2NH$ adduct, -19.3 k. cal. mole^{-1}. It is proposed that the incorporation of nitrogen into the ring of ethyleneimine forces the C—N—C angle to approach 60°. This prevents the nitrogen from achieving sp^3 hybridization in the addition compound. As a result, the nitrogen lone pair orbital does not overlap as effectively with the boron orbital as it would if it were hybridized sp^3. The boron-nitrogen bond is weak and the decreased donor strength of ethyleneimine is thus attributed to step VII of the cycle in Fig. 3–2. This phenomenon has been referred to as ring strain or internal strain (abbreviated I-strain). The general problem of the effect of ring size on the donor strength of an atom in the ring and also

of an atom bonded to the ring (*e.g.*, the oxygen in $\left[\begin{array}{c} CH_2 \\ | \\ (CH_2)_n \end{array}\!\!\!\!>\!\!C\!\!=\!\!O\right]$)
has been studied in detail.[3] This is a complex problem and is not completely understood at present. Donor strength can change if the hybridization of the donor atom and/or the atoms bonded to it are affected by the geometry of the rings.

It is interesting to compare the donor properties of $(CH_3)_3N$ and $(SiH_3)_3N$. Since silicon is less electronegative than carbon, it would be predicted on the basis of the inductive effect that the silylamine should be the better donor. An additional factor must be considered here, since silicon has empty d orbitals available to overlap with the filled p orbital on nitrogen to form a π-bond. The best π orbital overlap results if the three silicons and nitrogen are planar, and it has been shown by electron diffraction that these four atoms are planar. This π-bonding effect should lead to a decrease in the energy of step VII of Fig. 3–2 for the silylamine because there is less electron density on nitrogen (*i.e.*, the energy of the lone pair orbital becomes more negative). It should also lead to an increase in the energy of step VI because there is less π-bonding in the activated tetrahedral configuration than in the planar ground state. As a result of this π-bonding effect, which is absent in $(CH_3)_3N$, it would be expected that $(SiH_3)_3N$ should be a poorer donor than $(CH_3)_3N$. That $(H_3Si)_3N$ does *not* form an adduct with $B(CH_3)_3$ indicates that the inductive effect in this case is much less important than the π-bonding effect.

It is of interest to examine the results of studies on systems where donor atoms in different rows and columns of the periodic table are compared. The appropriate data are collected in Table 3–2. The difference in the donor strengths of $(CH_3)_2O$ and $(CH_3)_3N$ can be rationalized by application of the concepts already discussed. Oxygen is more electronegative than nitrogen, and the energy of its donor orbital relative to the acceptor orbital of boron in BF_3 is lower than that of nitrogen. Less covalency is expected in the oxygen adduct, and the bond energy is less.

The pyridine adducts (the last three compounds listed in Table 3–2) again indicate the existence of a steric effect. The inductive effect would predict that the substitution of a methyl group on the pyridine ring would increase the nitrogen donor strength, and indeed it is

---

[3] See, for example, D. E. McLaughlin, M. Tamres and S. Searles, Jr., *J. Am. Chem. Soc.*, **82**, 5621 (1960), and references contained in this article.

found that 4-methyl pyridine, H_3C—⬡N : , is a stronger donor

than pyridine. However 2-methyl-pyridine, ⬡N : , is a poorer

$$CH_3$$

donor than pyridine toward $B(CH_3)_3$ because of F-strain.

Table 3-2[a]

Enthalpies of Adduct Formation for Gas Phase Reactions

Adduct	$-\Delta H$	Adduct	$-\Delta H$
$(CH_3)_2OBF_3$	13.3	$(CH_3)_3PB(CH_3)_3$	16.4
$(CH_3)_2SBF_3$	Dissoc.[a]	$(CH_3)_3NB(CH_3)_3$	17.6
$(CH_3)_3NBF_3$	Too stable[a]	$C_5H_5NB(CH_3)_3$	17.0
$(CH_3)_3PBF_3$	18.9	$2\text{-}CH_3C_5H_4NB(CH_3)_3$	~10
$(CH_3)_3SbBF_3$	Dissoc.[a] at $-78°C$	$4\text{-}CH_3C_5H_4NB(CH_3)_3$	19.4

[a] Dissoc. indicates the compound is too highly dissociated to permit detection of the addition compound; too stable indicates complete association of the addition compound in the gas phase within the limits of detection.

When considering compounds of a series of elements in a given family of the periodic table, one notices that the donor strength toward the acids contained in Table 3-2 decreases in the orders $(CH_3)_3N > (CH_3)_3P > (CH_3)_3Sb$, and $(CH_3)_2O > (CH_3)_2S$. Even though the sulfur is not as electronegative as oxygen, and the phosphorus is not as electronegative as nitrogen, the phosphorus and sulfur compounds are weaker donors than the corresponding nitrogen and oxygen compounds. Two effects are probably operative which account for this order: (1) The dipole moments of $(CH_3)_3P$ and $(CH_3)_2S$ are considerably lower than those of the analogous nitrogen and oxygen compounds. As a result, there is a considerably smaller contribution to the bond energy from electrostatic interactions in the adducts of the compounds of the heavier elements. (2) The overlap of orbitals of first row atoms is greatest with orbitals of other first row atoms and is expected to decrease regularly when one proceeds down a family of elements.

At this point the reader may feel tricked. Although the effect described in (2) above was not pertinent to the previous discussion, certainly the electrostatic contribution to the bonding [the effect discussed in (1)] was not constant in all the other adducts discussed (*e.g.*, $(CH_3)_2OBF_3$ *vs.* $(CH_3)_3NBF_3$). However, in the systems discussed previously, the data could be rationalized on the basis of predicted changes in the covalent term whereas the electrostatic terms give the "wrong answer." This is indeed a sad state of affairs because it means we have explanations only after we have answers. Our models have very little predictive value. However, as we continue to examine systems, we develop an intuitive feeling for the relative importance of the various energy terms. By employing empirical approaches, it will be shown subsequently that these intuitive explanations can be put on a quantitative basis. Before developing this subject, other experimental approaches which provide information concerning donor or acceptor strengths will be discussed.

PROCEDURES FOR ENTHALPY MEASUREMENTS IN POORLY SOLVATING SOLVENTS

The number of systems that can be studied by the gas phase technique is quite limited. Ideally, at the temperature measurements are being carried out, the system should have a vapor pressure of 10 to 30 mm, in order that a pressure decrease can be measured with enough accuracy to give a meaningful equilibrium constant. Many solid or liquid adducts, when raised to the necessary temperatures to give these pressures, dissociate completely. Other adducts form such stable compounds that they do not dissociate to an appreciable extent before complex decomposition reactions occur. When these conditions prevail, gas phase enthalpies can not be obtained by the above technique. Thus there are a large number of systems that can not be studied in the gas phase but which can be studied in poorly solvating solvents. The two most commonly employed techniques for obtaining data on these systems are based on spectrophotometric or calorimetric procedures.

As an example of the spectrophotometric technique, consider the series of curves shown in Fig. 3–5 for the system

$$B: \; + I_2 \rightarrow B\text{---}\overset{\curvearrowright}{\underline{I}}\text{---}\underline{\overline{I}}|$$

where B : is a base. These spectral curves are plots of the amount of light absorbed by several samples at different wavelengths of light. Instruments called spectrophotometers are available which indicate quantitatively the amount of light absorbed by the sample, *i.e.*, the absorbance axis of Fig. 3–5, and plot this by means of a recorder as a function of wavelength.

It is seen that addition of a base to a solution of iodine in CCl_4 causes a pronounced change in the spectrum. Curve (1) is that of iodine in CCl_4, and curve 4 is essentially that of the adduct $B\text{---}I_2$.

Intermediate curves (2) and (3) correspond to mixtures of different amounts of iodine and complex. *Whenever there is a pronounced change in the spectrum of a substance (acid or base) upon complexation, this change can be used to calculate thermodynamic data.*

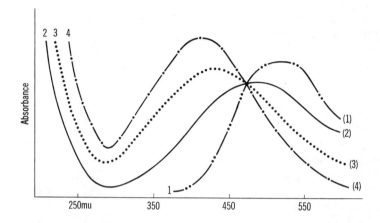

Figure 3–5 Spectra of Iodine and Base-Iodine Solutions. (1) I_2 solution in CCl_4, $8.30 \times 10^{-4} M$; (2), (3), (4) Same I_2 concentration but increasing base concentration in the order $2 < 3 < 4$.

For many substances, in a sample holder of a given dimension, a linear relationship exists between the amount of light absorbed and the concentration of substance. This relationship is given by the equation (referred to as Beer's Law)

$$A = \log_{10} I_0/I = [\epsilon][C] \tag{3-14}$$

where I_0 is the intensity of the incident light, I the intensity of the transmitted light (*i.e.*, the light not absorbed), and A, the absorbance, is simply the $\log_{10} I_0/I$. Most spectrophotometers directly plot absorbance as a function of wavelength. The concentration, C, is in units of moles liter^{-1} and the symbol ϵ corresponds to the molar absorptivity, *i.e.*, the absorbance of a molar solution of the material. If A is plotted *vs.* C for a series of different concentrations, ϵ is the slope of the straight line that should result, if the system obeys Beer's Law.

If the complex has an absorption peak with a known ϵ that does not overlap the peak from any other substance, the equilibrium concentration of the complex can be determined from equation 3–14 by measuring the absorbance. As described previously (see the section on Enthalpy Measurements by the Gas Phase Technique) if the initial concentrations of A and B are known and the equilibrium concentration of AB measured, the equilibrium concentrations of A and B are easily determined from the stoichiometry of the reaction, *i.e.*, for a 1 : 1 complex by subtracting [AB] from each initial concentration.

The following equation has been derived[4] for the rigorous spectrophotometric calculation of equilibrium constants for the formation of 1 : 1 acid-base adducts when ϵ cannot be measured directly, and when absorption peaks of the adduct overlap those of the acid or base

$$K^{-1} = \frac{A^T - A^0}{\epsilon_C - \epsilon_B} - C_A - C_B + \frac{C_B C_A}{A^T - A^0} (\epsilon_C - \epsilon_B) \qquad \text{(3-15)}$$

where at a given wavelength, A^T is the total absorbance, C_A and C_B are the initial concentrations of A and B (*i.e.*, the concentrations before reaction), A^0 is the absorbance corresponding to C_A or C_B, (whichever one absorbs), ϵ_C is the molar absorptivity of the adduct, and ϵ_B is the molar absorptivity of B (or if A absorbs and B doesn't ϵ_A is substituted for ϵ_B).

In many systems the adduct AB cannot be isolated so ϵ_C cannot be measured directly. When this is the case, there are two unknowns in equation 3–15, K^{-1} and ϵ_C. If two samples with different base concentrations are studied, the absorbance and base concentrations can be substituted into equation 3–15 to give two different equations. Since K^{-1} is the same in these two solutions and ϵ_C does not change, the two equations can be solved for K^{-1} and ϵ_C. As before, from the temperature dependence of K both ΔH and ΔS can be calculated. It should be emphasized that the above considerations are applicable to any spectrophotometric technique in which the absorbance is linearly related to concentration (*i.e.*, ultraviolet, visible, infrared, etc.).

The calorimetric technique[5] is based upon the measurement of heat evolved when the acid and base are mixed. A very simple calorimeter[6] design consists of a Dewar flask fitted with a Teflon lid, a stirrer, a fixed resistance, and a thermistor. The temperature change that occurs in the reaction is measured by a thermistor which is immersed in a solution of one of the reactants. The solution of the acid (base) is added to the solution of the base (acid) in the calorimeter, and the amount of heat evolved is measured.[5] The

---

[4] N. J. Rose and R. S. Drago, *J. Am. Chem. Soc.*, **81**, 6138 (1959).

[5] T. F. Bolles and R. S. Drago, *J. Am. Chem. Soc.* **87**, 5015 (1965).

[6] Designed by Professor E. M. Arnett of the University of Pittsburgh and described in *J. Am. Chem. Soc.* **87**, 1541 (1965).

amount of heat absorbed or evolved when the base (acid) solution is diluted, must be determined separately by adding the same amount of base (acid) to the solvent. This value is then used to correct the heat measured above. The heat liberated in forming an undetermined number of moles of AB can be measured in this way. If the equilibrium constant is known (for example, from a spectrophotometric study), the number of moles of adduct formed in the calorimeter experiment, and consequently the enthalpy change per mole of adduct formed, can then be calculated.

If the equilibrium constant is not known, the relationship between the heat evolved, the enthalpy of adduct formation (k. cal. mole^{-1}), and the equilibrium constant can be used

$$K = \frac{\dfrac{1000\,\Delta H'}{(v)\,\Delta H^0}}{\left(A_0 - \dfrac{1000\,\Delta H'}{\Delta H^0(v)}\right)\left(B_0 - \dfrac{1000\,\Delta H'}{(v)\,\Delta H^0}\right)}$$

where A_0 and B_0 are the initial acid and base concentrations, v is the volume of the solution in ml., $\Delta H'$ is the heat liberated on adding the acid or the base (corrected for the heat of dilution of the acid and/or the base), and ΔH^0 is the molar enthalpy of adduct formation. This equation can be simplified and rewritten

$$K^{-1} = \frac{1000\,\Delta H'}{(v)\,\Delta H^0} + \frac{A_0 B_0 \dfrac{v\,\Delta H^0}{1000}}{\Delta H'} - (A_0 + B_0) \tag{3-16}$$

There are two unknowns, K and ΔH^0. By measuring the heat evolved for two different base (acid) concentrations, two simultaneous equations result which can be solved for K and ΔH^0. The standard free energy and entropy can be calculated as before.

The equivalent of the gas phase enthalpy change can be obtained for almost any system, which is too stable to study directly using the gas phase technique, through a combination of gas phase and calorimetric procedures. The enthalpy change corresponding to

$$A_{(soln)} + B_{(soln)} \rightleftarrows AB_{(soln)}$$

is measured as described above. The heat of solution of liquid or solid A, B, and AB, is determined by measuring the heat evolved per mole of these substances added to the solvent. By measuring the vapor pressure of A, B, and AB as a function of temperature, the heat of sublimation $(A_{(s)} \rightarrow A_{(g)})$ or vaporization $(A_{(l)} \rightarrow A_{(g)})$ is obtained from the slope of the plot of log vapor pressure *vs.* $1/T$. The enthalpy changes for the following steps can now be added (where A, B, and AB are arbitrarily assumed to be solid or liquid).

$$A_{(soln)} + B_{(soln)} \rightleftarrows AB_{(soln)}$$

$$A_{(g)} \rightarrow A_{(s)}$$
$$A_{(s)} \rightarrow A_{(soln)}$$
$$B_{(g)} \rightarrow B_{(l)}$$
$$B_{(l)} \rightarrow B_{(soln)}$$
$$AB_{(g)} \rightarrow AB_{(s)}$$
$$AB_{(s)} \rightarrow AB_{(soln)}$$

$$\overline{A_{(g)} + B_{(g)} \rightarrow AB_{(g)}}$$

AB must be completely associated in the gas phase for this application, otherwise there are contributions to the *apparent* vapor pressure change of AB from the dissociation of the adduct into A and B.

FACTORS AFFECTING THERMODYNAMIC DATA OBTAINED IN SOLUTION

One of our first concerns is the nature of the species that exist in the solutions of polar molecules in nonpolar solvents, *i.e.*, how closely does this "situation" approximate the situation which one obtains in the gaseous state? In concentrated solutions of a polar solute in a nonpolar solvent, the polar molecules are appreciably associated. The heat of vaporization of many polar donors is greater than the heat absorbed when the donor is added to CCl_4 to make a dilute solution. (Entropy of mixing is often the main driving force which causes the donor to dissolve.) The difference is due to the fact that there is more association of the donor in CCl_4 than in the gas phase.

The effect of the association of a polar solute on the equilibrium constant for an acid-base reaction has been investigated.[7] The activity coefficient of N,N-dimethylacetamide [$CH_3C(O)N(CH_3)_2$, often abbreviated DMA] in CCl_4 was determined over the concentration range 0.01 to 0.39 M. The concentration equilibrium constant K for the reaction

$$DMA + I_2 \rightleftarrows DMA \cdot I_2$$

was studied over the concentration range 0.002 to 0.40 M in DMA for solutions 10^{-3} M in I_2. The K and ϵ_i values obtained for concentrated DMA solutions are the same, within experimental error, as those obtained for dilute DMA solutions even though the activity coefficient of DMA in this concentration range varies from 1.0 to 0.77. If the thermodynamic equilibrium constant, K_a, is written as

---

[7] R. S. Drago, R. L. Carlson, N. J. Rose and D. A. Wenz, *J. Am. Chem. Soc.*, **83**, 3572 (1961).

$$K_a = \gamma K = \frac{\gamma_1(\text{DMA} - \text{I}_2)}{\gamma_2(\text{DMA})\gamma_3(\text{I}_2)} \tag{3-17}$$

(where $\gamma = \gamma_1/\gamma_2\gamma_3$) then the ratio $\gamma_1/\gamma_2\gamma_3$ must be a constant over the concentration range 0.002 M to 0.40 M. Since I_2 is very dilute and nonpolar, $\gamma_3 = 1$ and γ_1/γ_2 must remain constant. Consequently, as long as the values of K and ϵ do not show a concentration dependence on going from very dilute to more concentrated solution, it may be assumed that γ_1/γ_2 is approximately 1, and a very close approximation to the thermodynamic equilibrium constant is obtained from these studies. It should be emphasized that the above study and resulting conclusions pertain to solutions that are still relatively quite dilute ($<0.4\ M$). An extension of these arguments to solutions much more concentrated than 0.4 M would require more research.

Next, we might ask what effect association has on the experimentally determined value of the enthalpy change. As long as the ratio γ_1/γ_2 does not change with temperature, the standard enthalpy change, ΔH^0, will result from studies of the temperature dependence of K. The change in γ for a substance as a function of temperature is related to the heat of solution by the equation

$$\text{R} \ln \gamma = \Delta H\,\text{soln}/T + \text{Constant} \tag{3-18}$$

Since the heat of solution (ΔH_{sol}) of most materials in CCl_4 is small, the difference in the heat of solution of two similar materials such as the base and the complex (*i.e.*, the difference in γ_2 and γ_1 at the two temperatures) should be even smaller and probably within experimental error for many systems.

The above arguments receive strong support from equilibria studied in both the gas phase and non-solvating solvents. The enthalpy of formation of iodine adducts measured in the gas phase[8,9] has been found to be, within experimental error, identical with the enthalpy of formation of the corresponding adduct measured in an inert solvent. However, in these and other systems [10,11] the equilibrium constant has been found to be highly dependent upon the inert solvent employed. Different equilibrium constants for a given adduct are found in CCl_4, hexane, and the gas phase. Evidently, the ratio of γ_1/γ_2 varies considerably with the inert solvent, but the temperature

[8] J. M. Goodenow and M. Tamres, *J. Chem. Phys.*, **43**, 3393 (1965).

[9] F. T. Lang and R. L. Strong, *J. Am. Chem. Soc.*, **87**, 2345 (1965).

[10] C. C. Thompson, Jr. and P. A. D. de Maine, *J. Am. Chem. Soc.*, **85**, 3096 (1963).

[11] R. E. Merrifield and W. D. Phillips, *J. Am. Chem. Soc.*, **80**, 2778 (1958).

variation of these activity coefficients (*i.e.*, the heat of solution) is relatively slight. These findings provide one of the strongest arguments for using enthalpy data instead of free energies as the criterion for the magnitude of the acid-base interaction.

The next question that arises concerns what constitutes a poorly solvating solvent. To answer this question a model donor-acceptor system was selected and thermodynamic data were collected in several solvents. The N,N-dimethylacetamide (DMA)—iodine adduct, which has been well characterized in carbon tetrachloride,[12] was studied[13] in the solvents methylene chloride (CH_2Cl_2), benzene (C_6H_6), dioxane,

$$\left[\begin{array}{c} CH_2\!\!-\!\!CH_2 \\ O \qquad\qquad O \\ CH_2\!\!-\!\!CH_2 \end{array} \right]$$

and 3 methylsulfolane

$$\left[\begin{array}{c} H \quad CH_3 \quad H_2 \\ C\!-\!\!-\!\!C \quad O \\ \qquad S \\ C\!-\!\!-\!\!C \quad O \\ H_2 \qquad\quad H_2 \end{array} \right]$$

Methylene chloride is a hydrogen-bonding solvent. Benzene is basic toward iodine, with a reported equilibrium constant for adduct formation of 0.15 liter/mole at 25°C in carbon tetrachloride.[14] In the absence of specific interactions, the solvating ability of a solvent is a function of the dielectric constant. Dielectric constants for these solvents are listed in Table 3-3. The dielectric constant of 3-methylsulfolane, which is also a donor solvent toward iodine, has not been reported in the literature but the value for sulfolane (tetrahydrothiophene-1,1-dioxide) is 44 at 30°C. Dioxane is a stronger donor toward iodine than is sulfolane and has a dielectric constant of 2.2 (25°C). The results tabulated in Table 3-3 were calculated by incorrectly assuming the solvent to be inert.

---

[12] R. S. Drago, R. L. Carlson, N. J. Rose, and D. A. Wenz, *J. Am. Chem. Soc.*, **83**, 3572 (1961).

[13] R. S. Drago, T. F. Bolles and R. J. Niedzielski, *J. Am. Chem. Soc.*, **88**, 2717 (1966).

[14] H. A. Benesi and J. H. Hildebrand, *J. Am. Chem. Soc.*, **71**, 2703 (1949). L. J. Andrews and R. M. Keefer, *J. Am. Chem. Soc.*, **74**, 4502 (1952).

Table 3–3

Thermodynamic Data for the System DMA-I_2 in Benzene, Methylene Chloride, and Carbon Tetrachloride

Solvent	Dielectric Constant (20°C)	K (l. mole^{-1} at 25°C)	$-\Delta H$ (k. cal. mole^{-1})
C_6H_6	2.28	2.57	3.3
CH_2Cl_2	9.08	1.47	2.6
CCl_4	2.24	6.9	4.0

The enthalpies in C_6H_6 and CH_2Cl_2 could be corrected to the gas phase value (*i.e.*, the CCl_4 value) if all the parameters in the following enthalpy cycle could be evaluated

$$\begin{array}{ccccc}
 & & \Delta H_{CCl4} & & \\
DMA_{(CC14)} & + I_{2(CC14)} & \rightleftarrows & DMA \cdot I_{2(CC14)} & \\
\uparrow \Delta H_B & \uparrow \Delta H_A & & \downarrow \Delta H_C & \\
DMA(solv) & + I_2(solv) & \rightleftarrows & DMA \cdot I_2(solv) & \\
 & & \Delta H_{obs} & &
\end{array}$$

where ΔH_{obs} is the measured enthalpy in the polar solvent and ΔH_B, ΔH_A, and ΔH_C represent the difference in enthalpy of solvation of the base, acid, and complex in the polar solvent and CCl_4. This cycle leads to the equation

$$\Delta H_{obs} = \Delta H_{CCl_4} + \Delta H_B + \Delta H_A + \Delta H_C$$

where ΔH_A and ΔH_B usually correspond to endothermic and ΔH_C to exothermic processes.

The question now is, "If physical limitations prevent one from working in CCl_4 and hexane, can one correct the data obtained in these other solvents to the equivalent of gas phase data?" The stumbling block is the evaluation of ΔH_C, which cannot be determined directly. However, for the data in Table 3–3 all of the quantities but ΔH_C can be measured directly. Consequently, this term can be obtained by difference and its magnitude evaluated; *i.e.*, one can determine if these solvents are poor solvating substances. When the enthalpy data obtained in benzene are corrected for the benzene-iodine interaction (ΔH_C) the corrected enthalpy is the same, within experimental error, as that obtained in CCl_4 (-4.1 k cal mole^{-1} compared to -4.0 k. cal. mole^{-1}). This indicates that the difference in the enthalpy of solvation of the base, ΔH_B, and the complex, ΔH_C, in benzene must be the same as those in CCl_4. Since the heats of solution of DMA in CCl_4 and benzene are approximately the same there must be very little difference in the enthalpy of solva-

59

tion of the complex, *i.e.*, the solvating properties of benzene and carbon tetrachloride are similar toward these materials. If this is true for most substances which are not Lewis acids, the range of systems which may be examined in poorly solvating solvents would be significantly increased, because many compounds which are not soluble in CCl_4 or hexane are soluble in benzene. However, it should be emphasized that a correction for the interaction of the acid with the benzene must be made.

The situation in CH_2Cl_2 is considerably different. Since the electronic spectrum of iodine in CH_2Cl_2 and CCl_4 are similar, it is assumed that iodine complexation makes no significant contribution to the enthalpy difference in these two solvents. Methylene chloride does hydrogen bond to DMA, so ΔH_b is appreciable in this solvent. When this interaction is incorporated a corrected enthalpy value of -4.9 k. cal. mole^{-1} is obtained. Since this is not equal to ΔH_{CCl_4}, the value of ΔH_c must be about -0.9 k. cal. mole^{-1}. Since methylene chloride probably does not form a specific, well-defined adduct with the DMA-I_2 complex, we shall attribute this -0.9 k. cal. mole^{-1} to nonspecific solvation of this complex. This enthalpy value is appreciable when compared to the differences in the enthalpy of formation of many adducts in the solvent CCl_4. In conclusion, data obtained in CH_2Cl_2 cannot be compared to data in CCl_4 unless a procedure for evaluating contributions from nonspecific solvation can be found.

Meaningful thermodynamic data could not be obtained in the solvents 3-methylsulfolane and dioxane. However, the results of these studies indicate that the reaction of iodine with various donors to produce I_3^- can be incorporated into the Coordination Model for nonaqueous solvent behavior.[15] This model focuses attention on the donor and solvating properties of the solvent in accounting for the extent of anion dissociation from a solute. In the donor-iodine system, it is found that strong donors, *e.g.*, $(C_2H_5)_3N$, displace iodide from iodine, resulting in the formation of I^+ (solvated) and I_3^- (see equation 1–37). In dilute solutions of the strong donor $(C_2H_5)_3N$, iodide is displaced even in the poor solvating solvent hexane. At the same molar concentration, DMA is not a strong enough donor to displace iodide. Toward iodine, 3-methylsulfolane is a weak donor with a measured enthalpy of adduct formation in

---

[15] R. S. Drago, D. H. Hart and R. L. Carlson, *J. Am. Chem. Soc.*, **87**, 1900 (1965).

CCl_4 of -2.3 k. cal. $mole^{-1}$. However, 3-methylsulfolane has a high dielectric constant and is expected to be a good solvating solvent, *i.e.*, one that will undergo nonspecific interactions with solutes and will facilitate charge separation. When iodine is added to 3-methyl-sulfolane (or when mixtures of DMA and I_2 are investigated in this solvent), extensive formation of I_3^- results. In contrast to this behavior, I_3^- is not detected when I_2 (or mixtures of DMA and I_2) are dissolved in pure 1, 4-dioxane as solvent. The enthalpy of formation of the dioxane-iodine adduct in CCl_4 is -3.1 k.[16] cal. $mole^{-1}$, so it is a better donor than 3-methylsulfolane. However, one would expect dioxane to be a poor solvating solvent. These observations indicate the importance of both solvent donor strength and solvating ability in accounting for anion displacement. When studying addition compound formation, one must be very careful to ascertain whether or not anion displacement is occurring.

In conclusion, it must be emphasized that solvent interactions make significant contributions to the measured enthalpy values of adduct formation. Specific interactions between the solvent and a reacting species significantly change the observed equilibrium constant and enthalpy; even contributions from nonspecific solvation have pronounced effects. Therefore, direct comparison of enthalpies measured in different solvents is not feasible. The interpretation of changes in the equilibrium constant with changes in solvent appears formidable at present. Until all the factors affecting the equilibrium constant are understood, it is extremely hazardous to interpret small differences between equilibrium constants measured in various solvents (solvating or poorly solvating).

INTERPRETATION OF SOLUTION ENTHALPIES

Our next concern will be with the kind of information that can be obtained from donor-acceptor studies. This will involve the interpretation of data that have been obtained using poorly solvating solvents. In view of the very large amount of data reported, only a small fraction can be covered here.[17]

---

[16] J. A. A. Ketelaar, C. van de Stolpe, A. Goudsmit, and W. Dzcubas, *Rec. trav. chim.*, **71**, 1104 (1952).

[17] The book by G. Brieglieb, *Elektronek-Donator-Acceptor-Komplexe*, Springer-Verlag, Berlin, Germany, 1961 (in German) covers most studies reported before 1961.

The donor properties of a series of compounds containing the carbonyl $\left(\begin{array}{c}\diagdown\\\diagup\end{array}C{=}O\right)$ group have been investigated in detail.[18] The enthalpies of adduct formation with iodine and phenol are listed in Table 3–4.

Table 3–4

Donor Properties of Some Carbonyl Compounds

Formula (Name)	$-\Delta H(C_6H_5OH)^a$	$-\Delta H(I_2)^a$
$CH_3C(O)CH_3$ (acetone)	3.7 ± 0.4	~ 3
$CH_3C(O)N(CH_3)_2$ (N,N-dimethyl acetamide)	6.1 ± 0.4	4.0 ± 0.1
$CH_3C(O)OCH_3$ (methyl acetate)	3.3 ± 0.4	2.5 ± 0.1
$(CH_3)_2NCON(CH_3)_2$ (tetramethyl-urea)	6.0 ± 0.4	4.3 ± 0.1

^{a} Enthalpy in k. cal. mole^{-1}.

On comparing the donor strengths of acetone and N,N-dimethylacetamide, (which have been shown to employ the oxygen atom in adduct formation) one sees the carbonyl oxygen is a much better donor in the latter compound. It has been proposed that the increased donor strength results from the fact that there is more electron density on the oxygen atom in the amide because of a resonance effect that is not possible in acetone. This can be illustrated by

$$CH_3\overset{\displaystyle\overline{O}\backslash}{\underset{}{C}}{-}\overline{N}(CH_3)_2 \leftrightarrow CH_3{-}\overset{\displaystyle|\overset{\delta-}{O}|}{\underset{\delta+}{C}}{=}N(CH_3)_2$$

It can be seen that the form on the right, which should be more important in the adduct than in the uncomplexed donor, places additional electron density on the oxygen. One might naively expect that if one $-N(CH_3)_2$ group attached to a carbonyl carbon leads to such a large increase in donor strength, two could be even better. By examining the data for $(CH_3)_2NC(O)N(CH_3)_2$ it can be seen that this is *not* the case. If the carbon atom is to pi-bond effectively with *both* the nitrogen atoms, the system

[18] R. L. Middaugh, R. S. Drago and R. J. Niedzielski, *J. Am. Chem. Soc.*, **86**, 388 (1964).

must be planar. This condition must be fulfilled because the N,O and C (carbonyl) atoms should each have a p orbital perpendicular to the molecular plane for effective π overlap. Inspection of molecular models shows that a steric effect in $(CH_3)_2NCON(CH_3)_2$ prevents all four methyl groups from lying in a plane. Consequently, both nitrogens cannot interact with the carbonyl in the same way that the one can and the carbonyl oxygen is not a better donor in $(CH_3)_2NCON(CH_3)_2$ than in $CH_3C(O)N(CH_3)_2$.

The OCH_3 group in $CH_3C(O)OCH_3$, methylacetate, should be capable of undergoing the same type of pi-bonding with the carbonyl group as the nitrogen atom in the amide. There is considerable evidence to indicate that this is the case. However, it can be seen from the data in Table 3–4, that methyl acetate, is not as good a donor as $CH_3C(O)N(CH_3)_2$. The reason for this is that the oxygen of OCH_3 is so electronegative that it withdraws more electron density by an inductive effect through the sigma bond than it releases to the carbon through the pi-bond (compare the donor strengths of acetone and methyl acetate). It is interesting to point out that N,N-dimethylacetamide is a good solvent for many acidic polar compounds whereas acetone and methylacetate are not. This can be attributed in part to the stronger donor properties of the amide.

Another set of data from which trends in acceptor strengths can be assessed is contained in Table 3–5.

Table 3–5

Acceptor Strengths of a Series of Lewis Acids
toward N,N-Dimethylacetamide[a]

	K (l. mole^{-1})	$-\Delta H$[b]	$-\Delta S^0$(e.u.)
I_2	6.9 ± 0.2	$4.0 \pm .1$	9.6 ± 1
ICl	1100 ± 100	9.5 ± 0.5	16 ± 2
SO_2	2.6 ± 3	3.3 ± 0.8	9 ± 2
Br_2	1.8 ± 0.4	1.6 ± 0.3	4 ± 1
C_6H_5OH	134 ± 3	6.4 ± 0.2	10.6 ± 1

[a] R. S. Drago and D. A. Wenz, *J. Am. Chem. Soc.*, **84**, 526 (1962); M. D. Joesten and R. S. Drago, *J. Am. Chem. Soc.*, **84**, 2037 (1962).
[b] Enthalpies of adduct formation measured in CCl_4 solvent in units of k. cal. mole^{-1}.

In all instances 1 : 1 complexes, in which coordination occurs to the carbonyl oxygen of DMA, are formed. The acids and the base do not undergo large changes in geometry upon complexation, so the differences in enthalpies are attributed predominantly to step VII of the cycle in Fig. 3–1. The structures of the adducts in solution are believed to be

B—Ï—Ï|, B—Ï—C̄l|, B—S⟨O/Ol⟩ , B—B̂r—B̄r|, and B—H—O⟨C₆H₅⟩

where B is the carbonyl oxygen of DMA.

It is proposed that the order for decreasing covalency (*i.e.*, ψ_{cov} of equation 3–13) is

$$ICl > I_2 > Br_2 \sim SO_2 > C_6H_5OH$$

The larger the molecule, the more easily the charge cloud is distorted and the easier it is for the acceptor atom to accept electron density from the donor atom; *i.e.*, the electron density "accepted" can be more easily distributed over the acid. On the other hand, the following order represents a decreasing contribution to the bond energy from electrostatic interactions.

$$C_6H_5OH > ICl > SO_2 \sim I_2 > Br_2$$

Toward the base DMA, both covalent and electrostatic contributions to the bonding are important, and any two acids can be compared by locating their positions in these series. For example, ICl is a better acceptor than phenol because there is less covalency in the phenol interaction whereas I_2 is a better acceptor than SO_2 because of greater covalency. The greater electrostatic contribution in SO_2 than in Br_2 accounts for the slightly greater acceptor properties of SO_2 toward DMA. It is interesting that toward benzene, a donor with no dipole moment, the importance of covalency predominates, and Br_2 is found to be a better acceptor than SO_2. Consequently, in predicting the relative acceptor properties, account must be taken of the donor in assessing the relative importance of covalent or electrostatic contributions to the donor-acceptor interaction. *Any order of donor or acceptor strengths must be established relative to a given donor or acceptor.* Reversals may be expected when orders toward different donors (or acceptors) are compared.

This same phenomenon is manifested in the donor strengths of $CH_3C(O)N(CH_3)_2$ and $CH_3C(S)N(CH_3)_2$, which are oxygen and sulfur donors respectively.[19] Toward phenol, $CH_3C(O)N(CH_3)_2$ is a stronger donor than $CH_3C(S)N(CH_3)_2$ ($-\Delta H = 6.1$ and 5.5 k. cal. mole^{-1} respectively). Toward iodine the donor strengths are reversed, that of $CH_3C(S)N(CH_3)_2$ being greater than that of $CH_3C(O)N(CH_3)_2$ ($-\Delta H = 9.5$ and 4.0 k. cal. mole^{-1} respectively).

[19] R. S. Niedzielski, R. S. Drago and R. L. Middaugh, *J. Am. Chem. Soc.*, **86**, 1694 (1964).

For these donors the electrostatic order is $CH_3CON(CH_3)_2 >$ $CH_3CSN(CH_3)_2$ and the covalency order $CH_3CSN(CH_3)_2 >$ $CH_3CON(CH_3)_2$. Toward iodine, covalency is more important, whereas toward phenol the electrostatic property of the donor predominates.* These same basic ideas have been incorporated into the so-called *hard* and *soft acid-base concept*.[20] Those acids or bases which, in the model discussed here, undergo predominantly electrostatic interactions are called hard acids or bases. Those acids or bases which undergo covalent interactions, and thus have their charge cloud distorted considerably relative to what it is in the free acid or base, are called soft. A general "rule" equivalent to the above discussion is that hard acids interact more strongly with hard bases than with soft ones, whereas soft acids interact more strongly with soft bases than with hard ones.

The donor properties of ammonia and the amines can also be rationalized with the model we have developed.[21] The enthalpies of adduct formation toward iodine and phenol are summarized in Table 3–6.

Table 3–6

Donor Strengths of Ammonia and Some Simple Amines

Amine	$-\Delta H$ toward I_2 (k. cal. $mole^{-1}$)[a]	$-\Delta H$ toward C_6H_5OH (k. cal. $mole^{-1}$)[15]
NH_3	4.8	8.0
CH_3NH_2	7.1	9.3
$(CH_3)_2NH$	9.8	9.3
$(CH_3)_3N$	12.1	9.5

[a] H. Yada, J. Tanaka, and S. Nagakura, *Bull. Chem. Soc.*, Japan, **33**, 1660 (1960).

It is proposed that as the CH_3 group is substituted for hydrogen on the nitrogen atom, the covalent bond forming ability of the amine increases, but the ability to form electrostatic bonds decreases. As mentioned above, covalency is most important for iodine, and this property dominates the trend in enthalpies manifested by the above donors toward iodine. Toward phenol, an acid for which electrostatic and covalent interactions are both important, the increasing covalent bond forming tendencies and the decreasing tendency for

---

* It should be emphasized that the model of covalent and electrostatic interactions is only one of several ways of arriving at the final electron distribution in the molecule. It has been selected for this treatment because it is very simple, conceptually.

[20] R. G. Pearson, *J. Am. Chem. Soc.*, **85**, 3533 (1963).

electrostatic bonding of the amines as CH_3 groups are added just about cancel each other. Consequently, little change in donor strength is observed for the alkyl amines toward phenol. The importance of covalency in this hydrogen bonding interaction is shown by the fact that CH_3NH_2 is a stronger donor than NH_3 toward phenol. It is interesting to point out that toward Ni^{2+}, an acid for which the electrostatic properties of the base are very important, NH_3 is a stronger donor than CH_3NH_2.[21]

AN EMPIRICAL QUANTITATIVE APPROACH TO PREDICTION OF DONOR-ACCEPTOR STRENGTHS

The above interpretations [19,20,21] of donor and acceptor strength suffer from the qualitative nature of the arguments and the apparent arbitrariness with which we focus our attention on whatever property gives the right answer. It would be much better if we could place these arguments on a quantitative basis even if the quantitative parameters are empirically assigned. The following treatment, which has been recently proposed,[22] has been found to apply to several acid-base systems.

The earlier qualitative interpretations of donor-acceptor interactions suggest a "dissection" of the enthalpy changes in terms of the equation

$$-\Delta H = E_A E_B + C_A C_B \qquad (3\text{-}19)$$

The parameters E_A and E_B are interpreted as the susceptibility of the acid and base, respectively, to undergo electrostatic interaction, and C_A and C_B are the susceptibility of the acid and base, respectively, to form covalent bonds. From our previous discussion, we expect acids with large values of E_A to interact strongly with bases having large E_B values. Correspondingly, acids with large C_A values should interact strongly with bases having large C_B values. The empirical evaluation of the constants of equation 3-19 in which the only directly measurable quantity is ΔH has been described in the literature.[22]

Setting E_A and C_A for I_2 equal to 1.0 and using reported values of E_B and C_B for the amines produces the results in Table 3-7. The calculated values of ΔH compare well with the experimental values given in Table 3-6.

[21] R. S. Drago, D. W. Meek, R. Longhi, and M. D. Joesten, *Inorg. Chem.*, **2**, 1056 (1963).

[22] R. S. Drago and B. B. Wayland, *J. Am. Chem. Soc.*, **87**, 3571 (1965).

Table 3–7

The C_B and E_B Constants for the Amines and the Calculated
Values of ΔH for the Formation of Amine-Iodine Adducts.

	C_B	E_B	Calculated $-\Delta H$ (k. cal. mole^{-1})
NH_3	3.42	1.34	4.8
CH_3NH_2	6.14	1.19	7.3
$(CH_3)_2NH$	8.68	.94	9.6
$(CH_3)_3N$	11.61	.59	12.2

Using the "amine" constants derived from this iodine data, the constants of other acids were determined. For example, the appropriate C_B and E_B values for ammonia and the methyl amines were used along with the phenol enthalpies (Table 3–6) to produce two simultaneous equations which are solved for the C_A and E_A parameters for the acid phenol. Values of 0.574 and 4.70, respectively were obtained. These parameters reproduce the experimental heats of reaction of phenol with the four amines to within the limits of experimental error. Two equations are needed to determine the constants and two serve as checks. This basic procedure was repeated for a large number of acids and bases (for which enthalpies were measured) to produce the constants contained in Tables 3–8 and 3–9.

Table 3–8

Base Parameters

Base	C_B[a]	E_B[a]	Base	C_B[a]	E_B[a]
C_5H_5N	6.92	.88	$(CH_3)_2SO$	3.42	.969
NH_3	3.42	1.34	$(CH_2)_4SO$	3.30	1.09
CH_3NH_2	6.14	1.19	$(C_2H_5)_2O$	3.55	.654
$(CH_3)_2NH$	8.68	.94	$(CH_2)_4O_2$	2.82	.68
$(CH_3)_3N$	11.61	.59	$(CH_2)_4O$	4.69	.61
$C_2H_5NH_2$	6.14	1.26	CH_3OH	1.12	.78
$(C_2H_5)_2NH$	8.76	.94	$CH_3C(S)N(CH_3)_2$	9.06	.064
$(C_2H_5)_3N$	11.35	.65	$(C_2H_5)_2S$	7.78	.041
$CH_3C{\equiv}N$	1.77	.533	C_6H_6	1.36	.143
$CH_3C(O)N(CH_3)_2$	3.00	1.00	$CH_3C_6H_5$	1.91	.087
$HC(O)N(CH_3)_2$	2.73	.97	$p(CH_3)_2C_6H_4$	2.31	.068
$CH_3C(O)OC_2H_5$	2.42	.639	$s(CH_3)_3C_6H_3$	3.04	.024
$CH_3C(O)CH_3$	.66	.706	$((CH_3)_3CO)PO$	1.81	1.09

[a] Phenol and I_2 data were used in the calculation of all these base parameters with the exception of those for acetone where phenol and methanol data were utilized.

Table 3–9

Acid Parameters

Acid	C_A	E_A	Source[a]
I_2	1.000	1.00	Methyl amines
C_6H_5OH	.574	4.70	Methyl amines
ICl	1.61	4.15	(composite of all ICl data)
*CH_3OH	.14	3.41	Pyridine, DMF
*C_2H_5OH	.032	3.91	Pyridine, DMF
$(CH_3)_3COH$	.095	3.77	Pyridine, DMF
*$HCCl_3$	.10	5.11	(Et)$_3$N, THF
$N(CH_3)_3$	1.76	5.77	Methyl amines
SO_2	.726	1.12	Pyridine, DMA
TCNE	1.51	1.68	p-xylene, Dioxane
C_6H_5SH	.174	1.36	Pyridine, DMF
*HF	0.0	17.0	Acetone, Diethyl ether

[a] Bases used in determining acid constants.
* Tentative values calculated from very limited data.

It is important to emphasize that the two simultaneous equations which are solved to give E and C must be "different." Iodine and phenol are quite suitable as reference acids for the solution of the base parameters because the ratios of E to C for the two acids are one and eight, respectively. If the data are used for two acids in which the E to C ratios are similar, accurate values of E and C for a base cannot be obtained. Consequently, with the data available, the parameters obtained for acids other than C_6H_5SH, ICl, SO_2, $B(CH_3)_3$, C_6H_5OH and I_2 are less certain.

Much of the reported data are used to evaluate the E_A, C_A, C_B and E_B parameters. The test of this treatment comes in the number of *independent* checks available and the consistency of the results with chemical intuition. Table 3–10 contains the data for those systems which constitute checks on the parameters in Tables 3–8 and 3–9. Most of the thirty base parameters in Table 3–8 were determined from the ΔH values for the formation of the iodine and phenol adducts. Of the twenty nine ΔH values in Table 3–10 twelve were needed to calculate E_A and C_A for the acids, and seventeen constitute checks.

Our next concern is the comparison of the results calculated by equation 3–19 with chemical intuition, bearing in mind that the

Table 3–10

Tests of the Acid and Base Parameters

Acid	Base	Calculated $-\Delta H$ (k. cal. mole^{-1})	Experimental $-\Delta H$ (k. cal. mole^{-1})
ICl	$CH_3C(O)N(CH_3)_2$	9.5	9.5
	$CH_3C\equiv N$	5.0	4.9
	$(CH_2)_4O_2$	7.4	7.5[a]
	$p\text{-}(CH_3)_2C_6H_4$	4.0	3.8
	$s\text{-}(CH_3)_3C_5H_3$	5.0	4.9
	C_6H_6	2.8	2.9[a]
SO_2	C_6H_6	1.1	1.0
	$s\text{-}(CH_3)_3C_6H_3$	2.2	2.2
	$(CH_2)_4SO$	3.7	4.0
	*$CH_3C(O)N(CH_3)_2$	3.3	3.3
	C_5H_5N	6.0	6.0
$B(CH_3)_3$	*NH_3	13.75	13.75
	*CH_3NH_2	17.64	17.64
	$C_2H_5NH_2$	18.10	18.0
	C_5H_5N	17.26	17.0
C_6H_5SH	*$HC(O)N(CH_3)_2$	2.4	2.4
	*C_5H_5N	2.0	2.0
	$((CH_3)_3CO)_3PO$	1.8	2.0
	C_6H_6	.4	.5
$(CH_3)_3COH$	$(CH_3)_2CO$	2.7	2.9
	$CH_3C(O)OC_2H_5$	2.7	2.9
	$(CH_2)_4O_2$	2.8	2.9
	*$HC(O)N(CH_3)_2$	3.9	3.9
	C_5H_5N	4.0	4.0
TCNE	*$(CH_2)_4O_2$	5.4	5.4[b]
	C_6H_6	2.3	2.6[c]
	$CH_3C_6H_5$	3.0	2.9[c]
	$p\text{-}(CH_3)_2C_6H_4$	3.6	3.6[c]
	$s\text{-}(CH_3)_3C_6H_3$	4.6	4.8[c]

[a] Approximate enthalpy obtained from the linear plot of ΔF versus ΔH.

[b] Approximately corrected for the dioxane-chloroform interaction taking ΔH equal to -3.6 k. cal./mole.

[c] Measured in CH_2Cl_2 and corrected by subtracting one-half the enthalpy calculated for the base-CHCl$_3$ adduct by using the data in Tables 3–8 and 3–9.

* Data marked with asterisks were used to calculate the E and C numbers for this acid.

reference $E_A = C_A = 1$ has been set for iodine. First note that most hydrogen bonding acids considered here have a larger electrostatic parameter (E_A) and a smaller covalent parameter (C_A) than iodine. It is interesting that with the limited data available, HF appears to have a covalent bonding affinity of zero, and a very large electrostatic term in agreement with chemical intuition.

The constants for I_2 and ICl indicate that ICl exhibits the greater covalent and electrostatic bond forming ability. The acid ICl has a dipole moment of 1.2 Debye, whereas I_2 has no ground state dipole moment (but we recall that these parameters refer to the properties of the acid and base in the configuration appropriate for bonding). Thus, it is anticipated that electrostatic interactions in ICl adducts would be much larger than for I_2.

As was discussed in a qualitative manner in conjunction with Table 3–5, covalency is not as important for SO_2 as an acceptor as it is for iodine. The C_B and E_B parameters for oxygen and the analogous sulfur donors are also consistent with the earlier qualitative interpretations of the donor properties of these substances. The qualitative trends in covalent and electrostatic bonding used to account for the order of donor strengths of the amines also is manifested in these numbers. Donors like benzene which do not have a dipole moment are found to have relatively low E_B numbers and high C_B numbers. It is encouraging that the numbers obtained from this correlation agree so well with the qualitative explanations which were proposed earlier for these systems (in the literature).

Tetracyanoethylene, $(NC)_2C{=}C(CN)_2$ (TCNE), an acceptor with no dipole moment, utilizes low lying empty π orbitals as acid orbitals and has, as anticipated, a large covalent bond forming susceptibility but a low electrostatic bonding ability. It is amazing that the equation can be applied to an acid with such a different kind of acceptor property.

The above correlation is relatively new and the limitations have not as yet been uncovered. More thermodynamic data are needed to provide further tests. Most of the acids and bases covered do not undergo large changes in geometry upon coordination. Consequently, the interpretation can be focused on step VII of Fig. 3–2. The acid $B(CH_3)_3$ is the only one in which the geometry of the free acceptor is quite different from that in the complex. In order for these correlations to apply to acids which undergo appreciable valence state changes in adduct formation, the energy necessary to hybridize the acid for every adduct (*i.e.*, step VI of Fig. 3–2) must either be the same or be very small, or vary linearly with the magnitude of the donor-acceptor interaction energy. It is most likely that in the case of $B(CH_3)_3$, the bond energy and the hybridization energy vary linearly. This rehybridization energy must be included in the E and C constants. It will be important to obtain data for those acids which undergo appreciable changes in geometry upon coordination in order to determine if this will pose a limit on systems that can be included.

Another interesting feature is observed for the $B(CH_3)_3$ adducts of the amines. If the parameters calculated for $B(CH_3)_3$ are used with E_B and C_B for $(CH_3)_3N$ to calculate the enthalpy for the boron trimethyl-trimethylamine adduct, the result is 8.2 k. cal. mole^{-1} higher than the experimental value. The low experimental value is attributed to a steric effect in the trimethylamine adduct which would not be incorporated in the E and C numbers. The difference between the calculated and experimental enthalpy change leads to a predicted steric effect of 8.2 k. cal. mole^{-1}, which is in excellent agreement with the reported[23,2] value of 7.8 k. cal. mole^{-1}. Steric effects, therefore, can prove a severe problem, and one must be careful to select systems for determining E and C numbers in which steric effects are absent.

Finally, it will also be interesting to obtain data on systems for which the enthalpies of adduct formation are much larger than those reported here. The data from such systems will indicate whether the parameters reported remain constant when a great perturbation is made on the acids and bases by coordination.

CORRELATIONS OF ENTHALPIES OF ADDUCT FORMATION WITH SPECTRAL CHANGES

The measurement of enthalpies of adduct formation is a tedious, time consuming process. If done properly it can take from three to four days to obtain a spectrophotometric enthalpy value, while possibly one equilibrium constant and enthalpy can be obtained in two days by the calorimetric procedure. Consequently, it would be advantageous if the magnitude of the change in some spectral property could be correlated with the enthalpy of adduct formation. The spectral property could be measured in about five minutes and the enthalpy determined from the correlation. Two such correlations, to date, have been reported in the literature.[24,25] The infrared spectrum of free phenol and a phenol adduct CCl_4 solvent is illustrated in

---

[23] H. C. Brown et al., *J. Am. Chem. Soc.*, **75**, 1 (1953).

[24] M. D. Joesten and R. S. Drago, *J. Am. Chem. Soc.* **84**, 3817 (1962).

[25] T. F. Bolles and R. S. Drago, *J. Am. Chem. Soc.* **88**, 5730 (1966).

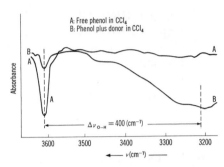

A: Free phenol in CCl_4
B: Phenol plus donor in CCl_4

$\Delta \nu_{O-H} = 400 \text{ (cm}^{-1})$

Figure 3–6 Infrared Spectra of Phenol and a Hydrogen Bonded Phenol.

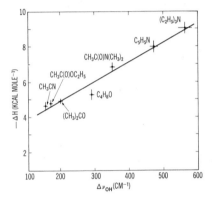

Figure 3–7 Correlation of $-\Delta H$ and $\Delta \nu_{OH}$ for Phenol Adducts.

Figure 3–6. The band at 3609 cm^{-1} is attributed to the O—H stretching vibration in phenol (*i.e.*, light of this wave length absorbed by phenol brings about an increase in the energy associated with the molecular motion of O—H bond). The band at 3209 cm^{-1} is attributed to the same vibration in the complex, and the shift has been attributed to adduct formation. It is found that if one plots the shift, $\Delta \nu_{OH}$, *vs.* the enthalpy of adduct formation, a straight line results over a certain range of the enthalpies. Fig. 3–7 illustrates the plot.

There are two very important points to be made about this plot that have not been realized by authors who disclaim the existence of this relationship. First of all, the limits of error on the correlation are ±0.4 k. cal. mole^{-1} (or at best ±0.2 k. cal. mole^{-1}). Any interpretation of enthalpies of adduct formation based on frequency shift differences that give enthalpies that differ by less than this is unsound scientific practice. The limits of error on the correlation results mainly from errors in the reported enthalpies. Even in the most carefully done study, it is impossible to obtain spectrophotometric enthalpies for phenol adducts any more accurately than ±0.2 k. cal. mole^{-1}. Better *reproducibility* than this can be obtained, but when one examines the error in ϵ at the temperature extremes and allows ϵ to change by this error at the two extremes (*i.e.*, K is calculated for the lowest and highest error limit at the two temperatures, the point being that a change of this magnitude would go undetected) an accuracy of better than ±0.2 k. cal. mole^{-1} cannot be claimed.

The second point to be made is that this correlation applies to enthalpies measured in the poorly solvating solvent CCl_4. For many weak donors the equilibrium constant is very small, and such large concentrations of the donor have to be employed to form appreciable amounts of the complex, that the solvent can no longer be considered to be CCl_4. Enthalpy data measured under these conditions may be expected to deviate from the correlation because of solvation effects. A clearly established exception to the $\Delta\nu_{OH}$—ΔH correlation has been reported[26] and an explanation has been offered.

One further word of caution is necessary regarding use of this correlation. If the base employed were extensively hydrogen-bonded to itself and if this hydrogen-bonding were destroyed on forming the phenol adduct, the measured heat would be the net of breaking the base-hydrogen bond and forming the phenol-hydrogen bond. The infrared frequency shift would reflect the enthalpy of forming the hydrogen bond to phenol and not the net, measured enthalpy. Referring to Fig. 3–2, breaking the self-hydrogen bonding of the base can be considered to increase the energy for base activation, step V. The change in infrared frequency is related to step VII. A straight line will result only if the measured enthalpy of adduct formation for the series of acids and bases used are linearly related to step VII. For example, if the acid (or base) is held constant, a correlation can be found only if the acid activation energy, step VI, (or step V, if the base is constant) is constant, negligible, or linearly related to ΔH. The above ideas should be kept in mind when seeking correlations of spectral shifts with enthalpies. The second reported[25] correlation involves the acid $(CH_3)_3SnCl$. The enthalpy of adduct formation correlates with the NMR tin-proton coupling constant.

The reader is cautioned against taking too seriously interpretations of infrared frequency shifts and changes in NMR (page 115) chemical shifts on the basis of donor-acceptor interactions when thermodynamic correlations have not been established. Both the chemical shift and the infrared frequency are complex numbers that depend upon many molecular properties. A theoretical analysis of the $\Delta\nu_{OH} - \Delta H$ correlation has been reported[27] indicating the requirements for a linear correlation. Many overzealous authors of journal articles feel they must interpret spectral changes in terms of coordinating ability and consequently guess at donor strengths suggesting orders that make everything work out well. Some of these will turn out to be correct, but many will not. The problem now is to determine which ones are correct, and this is impossible without thermodynamic data.

---

[26] R. S. Drago, B. B. Wayland, and R. L. Carlson, *J. Am. Chem. Soc.*, **85**, 3125 (1963).

[27] K. F. Purcell and R. S. Drago, *J. Am. Chem. Soc*, **89**, 2874 (1967).

CHAPTER 4

*Acid-Base Reactions in Water and
Other Highly Polar Solvents*

INTRODUCTION

In this chapter we shall survey two general types of acid-base reactions which occur in water and other highly polar solvents: proton
transfer reactions and the reactions of coordination compounds. As
in Chapter 3, our interest is focused primarily on the variation of
donor-acceptor properties (in terms of the thermodynamic functions
for simple reactions) with a change in the structure and nature of
the acid or base. However, for the reactions in polar solvents, the
problem is to separate the effect of structural changes from solvent
effects, because for most systems there is a lack of the appropriate
thermodynamic data needed to complete the cycles discussed in
Chapters 2 and 3. We shall discuss some of the approaches attempting
to circumvent these problems.

THE ACIDITY OF THE SIMPLE HYDRIDES

Superficially at least, there appears to be one property which exerts
a dominant influence on the ability of a compound to act as a proton
donor or Brønsted acid: the *electronegativity* or electron attracting
ability of the atom or group to which the proton is bonded. For example, HCl is said to be a strong acid and Cl^- a weak base because the
chlorine atom has a *large* electronegativity, whereas methane is said
to be a very weak acid and the methyl anion, CH_3^-, a very strong
base because the methyl group has a *small* electronegativity.

Although this interpretation of acidity and basicity in terms of
electronegativity is useful in a qualitative sense, it cannot be used to
predict acidities and basicities quantitatively or even to predict the
direction of the trend in acidities and basicities for certain series of
closely related compounds. For example, in Table 4–1 are listed the

approximate pK_a values for the series of acid dissociation reactions (Equation 4-1) of simple hydrides in water.

$$MH_{n(aq)} \overset{H_2O}{\rightleftharpoons} [MH_{n-1}{}^-]_{(aq)} + H_{(aq)}{}^+ \qquad \text{(4-1)}$$

Table 4-1 [1]

Approximate pK_a Values for Simple Hydrides, MH_n, in Water at 25°C

CH_4, 58	NH_3, 35	OH_2, 16	FH, 3
	PH_3, 27	SH_2, 7	ClH, − 7
		SeH_2, 4	BrH, − 9
		TeH_2, 3	IH, − 10

The trend of *increasing* acidity in the series, $CH_4 < NH_3 < OH_2 < FH$ and $PH_3 < SH_2 < ClH$, is just that which is expected because the electronegativity of the central element in the parent acids *increases* $C < N < O < F$ and $P < S < Cl$. On this same basis it would be expected that the acidity of the simple hydrides should *decrease* in the series, $FH > ClH > BrH > IH$ and $OH_2 > SH_2 > SeH_2 > TeH_2$, because the electronegativity of the central element in the parent acids also *decreases* in the same direction. However, the acidity of the simple hydrides *within* a given family of the Periodic Table *increases* with a *decrease* in the electronegativity of the central element. This observation, reemphasizes the discussion in Chapter 2 where it was shown that the dissociation of an acid in water is quite a complicated process. Obviously there must be some important energy terms which completely "swamp" the effects of electronegativity for the hydrides of the halogen and oxygen families. It is of interest to examine these energy terms for the hydrogen halides by means of the thermodynamic cycle presented in Fig. 4-1.

The thermodynamic functions which correspond to steps (1) through (4) of the cycle in Fig. 4-1 are listed in Table 4-2. The cycle is the same as that in Fig. 2-6 except that, for convenience, steps (b) and (f) of Fig. 2-6 are incorporated in step 3 of Fig. 4-1. The standard free energy and enthalpy changes accompanying the dissociation of the hydrogen halides in water, $\Delta G_4{}^0$ and $\Delta H_4{}^0$, are related to the simple processes in Fig. 4-1 by the equations

$$\Delta G_4{}^0 = \Delta G_1{}^0 + \Delta G_2{}^0 + \Delta G_3{}^0 \qquad \text{(4-2)}$$

$$\Delta H_4{}^0 = \Delta H_1{}^0 + \Delta H_2{}^0 + \Delta H_3{}^0 \qquad \text{(4-3)}$$

[1] R. P. Bell, *The Proton in Chemistry*, Cornell University Press, Ithaca, N.Y. (1959).

(ΔG_1^0 and ΔH_1^0, refer to the desolvation of HX; ΔG_2^0 and ΔH_2^0 to the dissociation of HX into ions; and ΔG_3^0 and ΔH_3^0 to the solvation of H^+ and X^-, respectively).

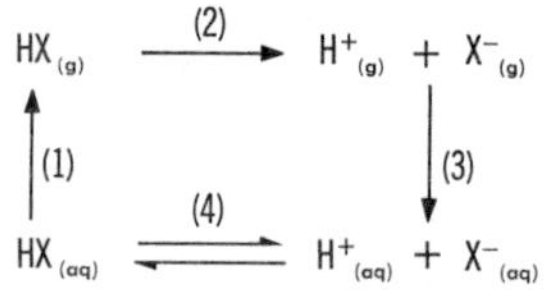

Figure 4–1 Thermodynamic Cycle Relating the Standard Free Energy and Enthalpy Changes for the Dissociation of the Hydrogen Halides, HX, in Aqueous Solution.

The data in Table 4–2 exhibit a number of interesting features. It is to be noted that because large positive values of ΔH and ΔG are associated with Step (2), none of the dissociation reactions will proceed to a measurable extent in the gas phase. However, for HCl, HBr, and HI the large amounts of energy available from the solvation of H^+ and X^- allow the dissociation reactions to proceed spontaneously to completion in aqueous solutions. For HF the dissociation reaction in aqueous solution does not proceed to completion because the free energy of the dissociation of HF into ions in the gas phase together with the free energy of desolvation of HF is *larger* than the free energy of solvation of H^+ and F^-. It is also noted that the *trend* in the values of ΔG_4^0, that is the trend in the acidities of the hydrogen halides in aqueous solutions, parallels the trend in the ΔH_2^0 values.*

---

* The thermodynamic quantities associated with step (2) of Fig. 4–1, which are difficult to obtain experimentally, are calculated from the following quantities which have been determined experimentally for the hydrogen halides.

(1) The normal bond dissociation energy of HX, De;
(2) The ionization potential of the hydrogen atom, I; and
(3) The electron affinity of the halogen atom, A.

These quantities refer to the processes

$$HX_{(g)} \rightarrow H_{(g)} + X_{(g)} + De$$
$$H_{(g)} \rightarrow H^+_{(g)} + electron + I$$
$$X_{(g)} + electron \rightarrow X^- + A$$

It follows then that the standard enthalpies for step (2) of Fig. 4–1 will be given by

$$\Delta H_2^0 = De + I + A$$

If the standard entropies and the values of ΔH_2^0, De, I, and A are compared, it is found that the trend in the ΔG_2^0 values is dominated by the trend in the values of De. Consequently it is often said that the trend in the acidities of the hydrogen halides in water is dominated by the trend in the normal bond dissociation energies.

Table 4–2

Thermodynamic Functions[a] for the Dissociation of the Hydrogen Halides by the Process Illustrated in Figure 4–1

	HF	HCl	HBr	HI
Step (1)				
ΔG_1^0	+5.	−1.	−1.	0
ΔH_1^0	+12.	+4.	+5.	+6.
ΔS_1^0	+23.	+18.	+19.	+20.
Step (2)				
ΔG_2^0	+360.	+324.	+314.	+304.
ΔH_2^0	+367.	+331.	+321.	+311.
ΔS_2^0	+23.	+23.	+23.	+23.
Step (3)				
ΔG_3^0	−362.	−333.	−326.	−318.
ΔH_3^0	−381.	−349.	−341.	−330.
ΔS_3^0	−63.	−54.	−50.	−40.
Step (4)				
ΔG_4^0	+3	−10.	−13.	−14.
ΔH_4^0	−2	−14	−15	−14
ΔS_4^0	−20.	−13.	−7.	0.
pK_a (calculated)	2	−7	−9	−10

[a] ΔG and ΔH in units of k. cal. mole.$^{-1}$ and ΔS in units of cal. deg.$^{-1}$ mole.$^{-1}$ (or entropy units, e.u.).

It is interesting that the trend in the free energies of solvation of the anions, which opposes the trend of dissociation energies in the gas phase, effectively decreases the *differences* among the free energies of dissociation in solution with respect to the corresponding gas phase reactions. In this respect it is important to emphasize that the trends in the acidities of these acids are complicated functions of the thermodynamic parameters for a series of simple reactions. The standard free energies of dissociation in water constitute *small* differences in large numbers, of which the solvation energies are predominant. Consequently, one is justified in concluding that the acidity of a species in a solvent such as water is as much a measure of the properties of the solvent as it is of the properties of the acid itself.

It is apparent that HCl, because of the large value of $K_a(10^{+7})$, is classified as a strong acid *in water*. However, the unqualified statement that HCl is a strong acid has little meaning. In solvents such as anhydrous formic or acetic acids in which the solvation energies of H^+ and Cl^- are smaller than in water, HCl is not completely dissociated. Using the criterion of the extent of dissociation, HCl would be classified as a weak acid in formic or acetic acid solvents. However, the acidity of the HCl (as measured by its ability to accelerate an acid-catalyzed reaction) is much greater in acetic acid than in water. The reason for this is that the acidic solvent, acetic acid, does not solvate the proton as effectively as the more basic solvent water. Consequently, the extent of dissociation is a meaningful criterion for acidity only when a specific solvent is considered.

The influence of the solvent is also exhibited in the values of the standard entropy changes for the dissociation reactions. For the gas phase dissociation reactions, the standard entropy changes are all positive as one might expect because two particles are formed from one and there is an increase in the *disorder* of the system. The entropy changes for the dissociation reactions in water, however, are negative, indicating an increase in the *order* of the system. The major cause of these negative entropy changes are the large negative entropies of aquation of H^+ and X^-. As discussed previously, the aquation of the proton can be considered to take place in two steps, the formation of the gaseous hydronium ion followed by its aquation.

$$H^+_{(g)} + H_2O_{(g)} \rightarrow H_3O^+_{(g)}$$

$$H_3O^+_{(g)} \xrightarrow{H_2O} H_3O^+_{(aq)}$$

Thus, in the dissociation of any acid HX in water, the proton is not really set "free" but is merely transferred from one base, the X^- ion, to another base, the water molecule. This, however, does not provide an explanation for the *decrease* in entropy associated with aquation. One source of this entropy decrease is the restriction of the translational and rotational freedom of the water molecules in the vicinity of the ions. In Fig. 1–2, a reasonable structure for the water molecules in contact with the hydronium ion in aqueous solutions is presented. Because there exists a large force of attraction between these dipolar water molecules and the hydronium ion, the solvent structure in the region of the hydronium ion is more "ordered" (that is, the individual water molecules are strongly oriented with respect to the hydronium ion and have less freedom to execute independent translations and rotations) than in pure water. For the same reason, the water structure in the vicinity of small anions like the F^- ion (see Fig. 4–2) is more ordered than that of pure water.

78

Although the appropriate thermodynamic data are not available at present for a detailed analysis of the acidity of the other simple hydrides, there is a limited amount of data for some of these compounds.

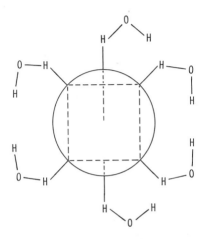

Figure 4–2 The Probable Orientation of the Water Molecules Surrounding the F⁻ Ion in Aqueous Solutions.

The estimated proton affinities of F^-, OH^-, NH_2^-, and CH_3^- are 367,[2] 375,[2] 395[2] and 405[3] k. cal. mole^{-1}, respectively. The results parallel the acidities of the parent hydrides. Thus it appears that the acidity is dominated by this step in the cycle. The expected effect of charge on the acidities of the hydrides is exhibited by the series $NH_4^+ > NH_3$ and $H_2O > OH^-$. This effect of charge is also reflected in the estimated[2]* proton affinities (k. cal. mole^{-1}): $H_2O(182) < O^{2-}(554)$.

---

* The upper limits to the proton affinities of NH_3 (172) and H_2O (151) have recently been obtained *via* mass spectral studies [3,4] and are more nearly in agreement with the earlier thermochemical estimates (200 and 170, respectively) by Latimer[5].

---

[2] T. C. Waddington, "Lattice Energies," in *Advances in Inorganic and Radiochemistry*, H. J. Emeleus and A. G. Sharpe, eds., Vol. I, Academic Press, Ind., New York, 1959.

[3] F. W. Lampe and J. H. Futrell, *Trans. Farraday Soc.*, **59**, 1957 (1963), Values contained therein.

[4] D. Van Raalte and A. G. Harrison, *Can. J. Chem.*, **41**, 3118 (1963).

[5] W. M. Latimer, *The Oxidation States of the Elements and Their Potentials in Aqueous Solution*, Prentice-Hall, Englewood Cliffs, N.J., 1952.

THE INORGANIC OXYACIDS

There are a number of regularities apparent in the variation of the acidities of the inorganic oxyacids. Although all the thermodynamic data necessary to subject these regularities to a detailed analysis are not available, it is of interest to present at least two of the explanations.

The pK values for the dissociation reactions according to equation 4-4 of a large number of inorganic oxyacids, of general formula $(HO)_mXO_n$, have been collected by Bell[1] and are listed in Table 4–3.

$$(HO)_mXO_{n(aq)} \rightarrow [(HO)_{m-1}XO_{n+1}]_{(aq)}^- + H_{(aq)}^+ \qquad (4\text{-}4)$$

Table 4–3

pK Values for the Dissociation of Inorganic Oxyacids in Aqueous Solutions at 25°C

Acid	pK	Acid	pK	Acid	pK
$(HO)Cl$	7.2	$(HO)NO$	3.3	$(HO)NO_2$	−1.4
$(HO)Br$	8.7	$(HO)ClO$	2.0	$(HO)ClO_2$	−1.
$(HO)I$	10.0	$(HO)_2CO$	3.9	$(HO)IO_2$	0.8
$(HO)_3B$	9.2	$(HO)_2SO$	1.9	$(HO)_2SO_2$	−3
$(HO)_3As$	9.2	$(HO)_2SeO$	2.6	$(HO)_2SeO_2$	−3
$(HO)_3Sb$	11.0	$(HO)_2TeO$	2.7	$(HO)ClO_3$	−10.
$(HO)_4Si$	10.0	$(HO)_3PO$	2.1		
$(HO)_4Ge$	8.6	$(HO)_3AsO$	2.3		
$(HO)_6Te$	8.8	$(HO)_5IO$	1.6		

It can be seen from Table 4–3 that the strength of the parent acid, $(HO)_mXO_n$, is related to the number of oxygen atoms, n, which do not bear hydrogen atoms. On the basis of their relative strengths, the acids fall into four groups exhibiting a general decrease in acidity in the series, $(HO)XO_3 > (HO)_mXO_2 > (HO)_mXO > (HO)_mX$.

There is a very simple explanation for the trends in the acidities of the oxyacids. This explanation has the added attraction of incorporating the solvent effects and of not requiring a separation of the enthalpy and entropy effects. The free energy change associated with the charging of a sphere of radius r, in a solvent of dielectric constant, ϵ, is given by, $e^2/\epsilon r$, where e is the charge placed on the sphere. If this same charge, e, is distributed among a number of spheres, n, of the same radius, then the free energy change is reduced to $e^2/(n + 1)\epsilon r$. Accordingly, if the net ionic charge of the anions of the oxyacids is considered to be distributed only among the oxygen atoms which do not bear hydrogen atoms, then at least a portion of the differences in the free energies of dissociation among the groups of oxyacids can be related to the free energy associated with distributing the net ionic charge among the oxygen atoms. Thus the larger the number of equivalent oxygen atoms which do not bear hydrogen atoms in the conjugate base (anion) of the acid, the smaller is the free energy change associated with the distribution of the anionic charge, and the stronger is the acid.

This same electrostatic argument is useful in explaining the large decrease generally observed in the successive acid dissociation constants of polyprotic acids. For a series of successive dissociation reactions such as those illustrated below, the dissociation constants decrease rapidly in the series, $K_1 > K_2 > \cdots > K_n$.

$$(HO)_n M_{(aq)} \rightleftharpoons (HO)_{n-1}MO_{(aq)}^- + H_{(aq)}^+ \qquad K_1$$
$$(HO)_{n-1}MO_{(aq)}^- \rightleftharpoons (HO)_{n-2}MO_{(aq)}^{2-} + H_{(aq)}^+ \qquad K_2$$
$$(HO)MO_{n-1\,(aq)}^{-n+1} \rightleftharpoons MO_{n\,(aq)}^{-n} + H_{(aq)}^+ \qquad K_n$$

This decrease in dissociation constants (or increase in the free energy of dissociation) should be readily understood. It is more difficult, for example, to separate a positive charge from an anion than from a neutral molecule. In terms of the previous discussion, it should be readily apparent that the free energy of dissociation would increase rapidly in the series above, since the free energy of "charging" the anion varies as the *square* of the anionic charge.

There is an additional effect which contributes to the enthalpy for the dissociation of the proton in these hydroxy acids; the relative *resonance stabilization energies* of the anions of the parent acid. Figure 4–3 shows a number of equivalent *resonance structures* for the NO_3^- ion; structures which differ only in the location of the electron pairs and *not* in the positions of the atoms or in the number of unpaired electrons. The combination of the normal sigma bond

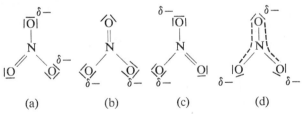

(a)　　　　(b)　　　　(c)　　　　(d)

Figure 4–3 Representations of the Resonance structures (a–c) and the Actual Structure (d) of the NO_3^- Ion.

and the pi (π) bond which arises from the "donation" of a lone pair of electrons from the oxygen atom to the empty p orbital of the nitrogen atom is designated by N=O in (a), (b), and (c). The *actual* structure of the nitrate ion (or the *actual* distribution of charge in the ion) is a hybrid of the resonance structures (a), (b), and (c) and is represented in (d) of Fig. 4–3. This structure incorporates the reasonable expectation that, since all the oxygen atoms in the NO_3^- ion are equivalent, each is capable of π bonding to the same extent and is capable of sharing the same fraction of the net ionic charge. Since the nitrogen atom in this ion has only one p orbital to participate in π bonding with the oxygen atoms, the π bond to any one oxygen atom must involve only the *partial* sharing of an electron pair. These equivalent π bonds involving the partial sharing of an electron pair are denoted by the dotted lines in Fig. 4–3, and the distribution of negative charge is indicated by the symbol for partial charge, δ^-.

Associated with each resonance structure of a molecule or ion is a characteristic energy. The *actual* structure is found to have a lower energy (that is to be more stable) than that associated with any resonance structure by an amount known as the resonance stabilization energy. It is also found that the magnitude of the resonance stabilization energy with respect to a given resonance structure increases as the number of resonance structures which contribute to the actual one increases. The NO_3^- ion, has a larger resonance stabilization energy than the free acid. Although resonance structures such as

$$H-\overline{O}=N\underset{\diagdown\,\,\underline{\underline{O}}}{\overset{\diagup\,\,\overline{\underline{O}}}{}}$$

contribute to the actual structure of the acid, they are considered less important than those given in Fig. 4–3. It is believed that the addition of a proton (which is electronegative) to an atom drastically reduces the ability of the latter to donate electrons by π bonding. Consequently, the gain of resonance energy in forming NO_3^- from HNO_3 should promote the dissociation reaction. In general, it is expected that the larger the resonance stabilization energy of the base relative to the free acid, the more negative is ΔH and the more favorable is the dissociation reaction. It should be pointed out that these arguments are related to the simple electrostatic ones presented earlier, in that resonance provides a mechanism for distributing the anionic charge. Thus, in agreement with the observed trend in acidities, the anion resonance stabilization energy is expected to decrease in the series

$$MO_4^- > (HO)_{m-1}MO_3^- > (HO)_{m-1}MO_2^- > (HO)_{m-1}MO^-$$

It is extremely difficult to interpret small differences in pK units in terms of structural parameters. The large difference among the acidities of these groups of oxyacids may arise primarily from an enthalpy effect, since the standard entropies of dissociation, which are known for a number of acids, generally fall within the range -15 to -21 cal. deg^{-1} mole^{-1}. The maximum contribution that such a variation in entropies could make to the dissociation constant is approximately 2 pK units. Because of this variation in entropy, a discussion of the trends in the acidity *within* a given group on the basis of enthalpy changes is not meaningful. Even if the enthalpies were determined experimentally it would still be necessary to evaluate the enthalpies of aquation of the various species (gas phase to solution). The fact that most of these species do not exist in the gas phase renders this impossible.

In conclusion, we should emphasize the complexity of these reactions relative to those discussed in Chapter 3. The lack of appropriate data for the various energy terms has caused many chemists to accept "explanations" which are very highly qualified and lacking in rigor.

ORGANIC ACIDS

Of all the protonic acids, the organic acids have been studied most extensively, and as a series of closely related compounds they provide an opportunity to interpret with a good degree of confidence the influence of structural variations on the free energy changes which occur in proton transfer reactions.

The pK_a values for the dissociation of acetic acid and ethanol in water at 25°C are 4.8 and approximately 15.8, respectively. The difference in the pK_a values seems too large to be attributed solely to solvation effects (i.e., to the difference in the free energies of solvation of $CH_3CO_2{}^-$ and $CH_3CH_2O^-$). If it is assumed that the net charge of the conjugate base is localized mainly on the electronegative oxygen atom(s), then in terms of the previous discussion the free energy of "charging" the acetate ion, which contains two equivalent oxygen atoms, should be *less* than that of the ethoxide ion.

An argument based on relative resonance stabilization energies leads to the same conclusion. The two important equivalent resonance structures which contribute to the ground state of the acetate ion are represented in Fig. 4-4(a) and (b), and the final charge distri-

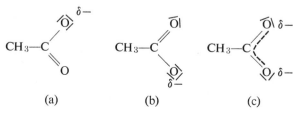

(a)   (b)   (c)

Figure 4-4 Resonance Structures of the Acetate Ion.

bution is indicated in Fig. 4–4(c). In the ground state of acetic acid itself, the two structures shown in Fig. 4–5 are not equivalent since the form on the right is of significantly higher energy than the form

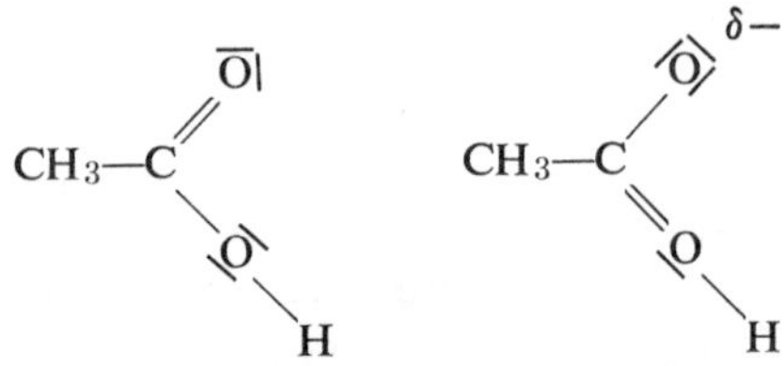

Figure 4–5 Resonance Structures of Acetic Acid.

on the left. Accordingly, resonance stabilizes acetic acid less than the acetate ion. Such resonance structures, of course, are not possible for either ethanol or the ethoxide ion. Both the electrostatic and resonance effects are acting cooperatively.

There is also a more subtle structural influence which is at work in these systems, and it warrants some discussion. Jaffe and co-workers,[6] on the basis of their calculations of *valence-state electronegativities*, have concluded that the electronegativity which an element exhibits toward substituents increases linearly with the amount of s character in the bonds by which the element is attached to the substituents. This conclusion is at least in qualitative accord with the experimental data which are available.[7] For example, acidities decrease in the series, acetylene ($HC\equiv CH$) > ethylene ($H_2C=CH_2$) > ethane (H_3CCH_3), in which carbon exhibits the valence states, sp, sp^2, and sp^3, respectively. Accordingly it can be said that acetic acid is more acidic than ethanol because the hydroxyl group in the former is attached to a more electronegative substituent, $--C\overset{O}{\underset{}{\diagup\kern-0.5em\diagdown}}$, containing carbon in an sp^2 valence state. It will be recalled that the function of the electronegative substituent is to aid in the dissipation of the net charge transferred in the acid-base reaction.

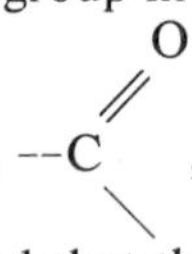

In a sense, the arguments we have advanced here are useful in the comparisons of species whose acidities are quite dissimilar. In such comparisons we certainly recognize that, although the data generally encompass large solvation and entropy terms, the *gross* regularities can be traced to unique structural features of the acid or base. Ulti-

[6] J. Hinze, M. A. Whitehead, and H. H. Jaffe, *J. Am. Chem. Soc.*, **85**, 148 (1963).
[7] H. A. Bent, *Chem. Rev.*, **61**, 275 (1961).

mately, it is these structural features which are our main concern whether we define the properties of acids (bases) in terms of acceptor (donor) strengths or acidities (basicities). We do encounter a number of difficulties, however, in attempting to analyze small differences in structural terms.

Thus we might ask what unique feature of the substituents, X, "causes" the variation in the acidities of the acetic acid derivatives, XCH_2CO_2H, listed in Table 4–4[8]. A correlation of pK_a with electro-

Table 4–4

Acidities of Acetic Acid Derivatives, XCH_2CO_2H, in Water at 25°C.

X	pK_a	X	pK_a
H—	4.76	$\overset{+}{H_3N}CH_2$—	3.60
CH_3—	4.88	$\overset{+}{H_3N}CH_2CH_2$—	4.23
$H_2C{=}CH$—	4.4	$\overset{+}{H_3N}CH_2CH_2CH_2$—	4.27
C_6H_5—	4.31	$ClCH_2$—	4.08
$N{\equiv}C$—	2.47	$ClCH_2CH_2$—	4.52
F—	2.59	$NCCH_2$—	3.99
Cl—	2.87	$NCCH_2CH_2$—	4.44
Br—	2.90	$BrCH_2$—	4.02
I—	3.18	$BrCH_2CH_2$—	4.58
$\overset{+}{H_3N}$—	2.31	ICH_2—	4.06
$(CH_3)_3\overset{+}{N}$—	1.83	ICH_2CH_2—	4.64
O_2N—	1.68		
HO—	3.83		
CH_3O—	3.53		

negativity seems obvious. But in what *sense* does the electronegativity of the substituent affect pK_a? It should be noted that the differences among the values are relatively small.--Recall that a difference of 1 in pK amounts to a difference of only 1.43 k. cal. mole^{-1}. in ΔF^0. The electronegativity can affect these pK_a values in at least three ways. First, by the operation of the *inductive effect* through the σ bonding framework, the substituent aids in the dissipation of the charge "created" in the carboxyl group when the acid ionizes. Second,

---

[8] pK_a values taken from the compilation by H. C. Brown, D. H. McDaniel, and O. Haflinger in E. A. Braude and F. C. Nachod ed., *Determination of Organic Structures by Physical Methods*, Academic Press Inc., New York, 1955, Chapter 4.

associated with all the substituents more electronegative than carbon is a dipole which, because its positive end is nearer the acidic center than the negative end, can stabilize the anion more than the parent acid. This electrostatic interaction operates directly "through space" in contrast to the normal inductive effect and has been termed the *field effect*. It has been treated quantitatively with acceptable results by Kirkwood and Westheimer.[9] Finally, it is possible that the electronegative substituents, by creating a dipole adjacent to the acidic center, affect the solvation energies of the parent acids or the anions sufficiently to account for these small differences in pK_a values. (This effect is closely related, but not identical, to the field effect outlined above.) It must be emphasized that any, or a combination of all three of these effects, may be the "cause" of the variation in pK_a values.

In this context it is noteworthy that the electronegative substituents, CN and F, have nearly as large an effect on the pK_a values as the *positively charged* substituents, NH_3^+ or $(CH_3)_3N^+$. This by itself, of course, does not suggest that field effects are absent. The possible intervention of *specific* solvent effects is reflected in the observation that although the substituent, $(CH_3)_3N^+$, should be less "electronegative" than NH_3^+ (H is considered more electronegative than CH_3), $(CH_3)_3\overset{+}{N}CH_2CO_2H$ is actually a stronger acid than $H_3\overset{+}{N}CH_2CO_2H$. Hydrogen bonding interactions of the type $H_2O \ldots HN\overset{+}{H}_2CH_2CO_2H$, should stabilize the parent acid relative to the anion. A similar effect is noted for the acids bearing the —OH and —OCH_3 substituents.

It might seem that a comparison of the pK_a values of structurally related substituted acetic acids, $X(CH_2)_nCO_2H$, should allow a separation of the substituent effects into inductive and field effects. Since the inductive effect depends on the transmission or polarization of electron density through relatively nonpolarizable C—C bonds, we would expect that the inductive effect should fall off much more rapidly with the distance of the substituent from the CO_2H group than would the field effect. In addition, on the basis of a simple model for the field effect, which involves the electrostatic interaction of the substituent with the "dissociating" proton, it would be expected that the relative pK_a values of the acids, $X(CH_2)_nCO_2H$, should be pro-

---

[9] (a) J. G. Kirkwood and F. H. Westheimer, *J. Chem. Phys.*, **6**, 605, 513 (1938); F. H. Westheimer and M. W. Shookhoff, *J. Am. Chem. Soc.*, **61**, 555 (1939); but see also

(b) J. D. Roberts and W. T. Moreland, *J. Am. Chem. Soc.*, **75**, 2167 (1953).

portional to $\dfrac{1}{r^2}$ if X is a dipolar substituent, but be proportional to $\dfrac{1}{r}$ if X is a charged substituent. (*r* represents the distance of the substituent from the proton of the CO_2H group.) However, it is readily apparent from an inspection of the data in Table 4–4, that the rate of decrease of the pK_a values for charged substituents with respect to n is not significantly different from that for dipolar substituents. Furthermore, the rate of decrease for the dipolar substituents exhibits no apparent trend with electronegativity.

Because it is possible that compensating changes in ΔH and ΔS may "smooth out" the pK_a values, it is legitimate to inquire whether a comparison of ΔH values might be less ambiguous. It would, indeed, but apart from the limited data available, there are problems inherent in interpreting the ΔH values for the reactions of acids and bases in polar solvents. In Table 4–5 are collected the thermodynamic data

Table 4–5

Thermodynamic Data for the Ionization of Cyanoacetic Acid in Water

Temperature, °C	5	10	15	20	25
ΔH^0, k. cal. mole^{-1}	−0.03	−0.28	−0.50	−0.71	−0.89
ΔS^0, entropy units	−11.30	−12.19	−12.96	−13.66	−14.28
ΔG^0, k. cal. mole^{-1}	3.11	3.17	3.23	3.30	3.37

for the ionization of cyanoacetic acid,[10] $CNCH_2CO_2H$. It is seen that ΔH^0 is dependent on the temperature. Despite this temperature dependence of ΔH^0, a plot of log K vs. $1/T$ is *linear* because of compensating changes in ΔS^0. This behavior is not particularly exceptional for the reactions of ions in highly polar solvents[11,12,13], and is most likely associated with the changes in the solvent structure and the structure of the solvation spheres of the ions as a function of temperature. It is this incorporation of changes in the solvent structure into the thermodynamic data for acid-base reactions in highly polar solvents that renders difficult the interpretation of small differences in acidities (basicities) in terms of the properties of the acid (base) alone.

---

[10] F. S. Feates and D. G. Ives, *J. Chem. Soc.*, 2798, (1956).

[11] D. H. Everett, D. A. Landsmann and B. R. W. Pinset, *Proc. Royal Soc.* (London), **A215**, 403 (1952).

[12] D. J. G. Ives and J. H. Pryor, *J. Chem. Soc.*, 2104 (1955).

[13] J. Jordan, *Record Chem. Progress*, **19**, 193 (1958).

Table 4-6

pKa Values in Water at 25°C for Benzoic Acids ($XC_6H_4CO_2H$), Phenyl Acetic Acids ($XC_6H_4CH_2CO_2H$), Anilinium Ions ($XC_6H_4NH_3^+$), and Phenols (XC_6H_4OH)

Substituent X	pK_a Benzoic Acid[8,1]			pK_a Phenylacetic Acid[14]			pK_a Anilium Ion[15]			pK_a Phenol[16,17]		
	meta	para	ortho	meta	para	ortho	meta	para	ortho	meta	para	ortho
H	4.21	4.21	4.21	4.31	4.31	4.31	4.58	4.58	4.58	10.02	10.02	10.02
CH₃	4.28	4.34	3.91	—	4.37	—	4.67	5.07	4.38	10.10	10.28	10.33
C₆H₅	4.15	4.20	—	—	—	3.46	—	—	—	—	—	—
CN	3.60	3.55	—	—	4.25	—	—	—	—	9.20	—	—
F	3.87	4.15	3.27	4.14	4.19	4.07	3.38	4.52	—	9.02	9.28	8.53
Cl	3.83	3.99	2.93	—	4.19	4.05	3.32	3.81	2.62	9.06	9.43	8.42
Br	3.81	4.00	2.87	4.16	4.18	4.04	—	—	—	9.10	9.38	—
I	3.86	3.93	2.87	—	—	—	—	—	—	—	—	—
NO₂	3.45	3.44	2.18	3.97	3.85	4.00	2.45	0.98	−0.30	8.35	7.15	7.22

[14] R. A. Robinson and R. H. Stokes, *Electrolyte Solutions*, Butterworths Scientific Publications, London, 1959. Values collected therein.

[15] M. Kilpatrik and C. A. Arenberg, *J. Am. Chem. Soc.*, **75**, 3812 (1953).

[16] C. M. Hudson and M. Kilpatrik, *J. Am. Chem. Soc.*, **71**, 3110, 3115 (1949).

[17] J. E. Leffler and E. Grunwald. *Rates and Equilibria of Organic Reactions*, John Wiley and Sons, Inc., New York, 1963. Values collected therein.

Nonetheless, the regularities observed in the trends of pK values for some acids can be placed on a quantitative basis. In Table 4–6 are listed the pK_a values, in water, for a variety of *ortho-*, *meta-*, and *para-* substituted benzoic acids, as well as those for substituted phenylacetic acids ($XC_6H_4CH_2CO_2H$), anilinium ions ($XC_6H_4NH_3^+$), and phenols (XC_6H_4OH). Again it is to be noted that, although the range of pK_a values for the given series of acids is small, a gross trend is apparent in the acidity with respect to the "electron withdrawing" power of the substituent. Indeed, if, as shown in Fig. 4–6, the pK_a values for the *meta-* and *para-*substituted acids of one structural type are plotted *vs.* those for another structural type, the points (with the exception of those for the nitro derivatives) fall along a straight line.

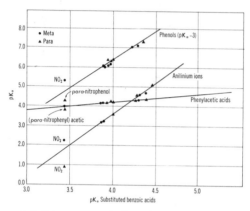

Figure 4–6 Linear Correlation of ρK_a Values in Table 4–7.

These linear correlations suggest that the changes in the free energies of ionization are proportional to some *common property* of the substituents. Hammett[18] found that this proportionality effect, which extends to the changes produced by *meta-* and *para-*substituents in a variety of equilibria involving substituted phenyl compounds, can be expressed in terms of linear free energy relationships of the type

$$\Delta G_x^0 - \Delta G_0^0 = \delta \Delta G = \rho \sigma_x \tag{4-5}$$

or

$$\log \frac{K_x}{K_0} = \rho \sigma_x \tag{4-6}$$

where, for example, in the ionization of *meta-* and *para-*substituted benzoic acids: ΔG_x^0 represents the standard free energy change in the

---

[18] L. P. Hammett, *Physical Organic Chemistry*, McGraw Hill Book Company, New York, N.Y., 1940; *Chem. Rev.*, **17**, 125 (1935).

ionization of the acid having the substituent X and ΔG_0^0 that for the unsubstituted acid; K_x and K_0 represent the corresponding equilibrium constants; ρ is a constant which reflects the sensitivity of the acid to the substituent effect which, in turn, is reflected in the value of the substituent constant, σ_x. The interaction constants, σ and ρ, are defined in terms of the ionization of benzoic acid in water at 25°C, for which the ρ value is set equal to 1. Thus it is possible to obtain values of σ_x^{meta} and σ_x^{para} for any substituent from the ionization constants of the appropriate benzoic acids, that is

$$\sigma_x = \log \frac{(K_{\text{XC}_6\text{H}_4\text{CO}_2\text{H}}^0)}{(K_{\text{C}_6\text{H}_5\text{CO}_2\text{H}}^0)} \qquad (4\text{--}7)$$

Accordingly, for the substituents C_6H_5 and I, the σ^{meta} values $+0.06$ and $+0.35$, respectively, are obtained from the data in Table 4–6.

From an inspection of the list of the σ values collected in Table 4–7, it seems reasonable to interpret the substituent constants as a measure

Table 4–7

Substituent Constants[19]

Substituent	σ^{meta}	σ^{para}
CH_3—	-0.069	-0.170
CH_3CH_2—	-0.07	-0.151
$(CH_3)_3C$—	-0.10	-0.197
C_6H_5—	$+0.06$	-0.01
F_3C—	0.43	$+0.54$
NC—	0.56	0.660
$\begin{matrix} O \\ \parallel \\ CH_3C\text{—} \end{matrix}$	0.376	0.502
O_2N—	0.710	0.778
CH_3O—	0.115	-0.268
HO—	0.121	-0.37
H_2N—	-0.16	-0.66
F—	0.337	0.062
Cl—	0.373	0.227
Br—	0.391	0.232
I—	0.352	0.18

[19] From the compilation in D. H. McDaniel and H. C. Brown, *J. Org. Chem.*, **23**, 420 (1958). Many of these values were obtained not from the ionization constants of benzoic acids, but from some secondary process such as the ionization of anilinium ions, the ρ value for which was evaluated from correlation lines like those in Fig. 4–6.

of the ability of the substituent to change the electron density at the reacting center. On this basis substituents having negative σ values are said to be more "electron releasing" than hydrogen whereas those with positive values are said to be more "electron withdrawing." It is advantageous at this point to discuss the trend in σ values at some length before briefly discussing the trends of ρ values.

As in the discussion of the variation of the acidities of substituted acetic acids, the trend in σ values must be considered in terms of the influence of at least four effects: (1) resonance effects; (2) inductive effects; (3) field effects; and (4) solvent effects. Because of the existence of the linear free energy relationships for the substituted benzene derivatives, however, a special restraint is imposed upon our interpretation of the substituent effects—either the σ values are dominated by one effect or the effects are, at least approximately, linearly related.

As occurs so frequently in chemistry, the points which *deviate* from the smooth correlation are quite informative. In each case, the deviation of the points for the *para*-nitro derivatives from the linear free energy relationship is pronounced, especially for the anilinium ions and phenols. It is generally found that other *para*-substituents which, like the NO_2 group, have acceptor orbitals of low energy (*e.g.*,

$$-C{\equiv}\overset{\oplus}{N}I{\leftrightarrow}\overset{\nwarrow\overset{\curvearrowleft}{O}\nearrow}{\underset{}{C}}{=}\underset{\ominus}{\underline{N}}I; \text{ and } -\overset{\overset{\displaystyle \|}{\overset{}{O}}}{C}-CH_3{\leftrightarrow}-\overset{\overset{\displaystyle |}{\overset{}{\underline{\overline{O}}}I\ominus}}{\underset{\oplus}{C}}-CH_3)$$ cause similar de-

viations. For these species a resonance interaction is possible, illustrated in Fig. 4–7, which stabilizes the conjugate base (the anion) more than the parent acid. Due to the high energy of suitable acceptor orbitals of the substituent, such a resonance interaction should be very small for the other phenol and aniline derivatives in Table 4–6. It should be absent for *para*-nitrobenzoic acid because

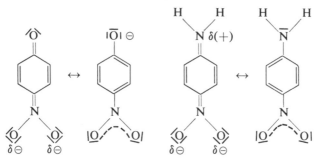

Figure 4–7 Illustration of the Resonance Interaction Which Stabilizes the Conjugate Bases of the *para*-Nitro-anilinium Ion and *para*-Nitrophenol.

the carboxyl group is itself an electron acceptor, *i.e.,*

In addition, since the resonance effects such as those shown in Fig. 4–7 are not possible for the phenylacetic acids,* we can conclude

(1) the correlation curves of Fig. 4–6 do not incorporate significant resonance effects; and

(2) the acidities of the *para*-nitro-substituted phenol and anilinium ion should, as observed, be greater than those predicted by the correlation of Fig. 4–6.

At the very least, the linear correlations in Fig. 4–6 provide a means of detecting relatively large resonance effects. Thus, although the *direction* of the deviation of the points for the *meta*-nitro derivatives from the correlation lines is difficult to explain, the *magnitude* seems to require the intervention of resonance structures such as

---

* The deviation of the point for *para*-nitrophenylacetic acid from the linear correlation, although small, is probably significant and could be rationalized through the intervention of a hyperconjugation resonance structure,

92

Even if, for a series of substituents, the resonance substituent effect can be neglected, it is impossible at this point to analyze σ values quantitatively in terms of the three remaining effects. Solvent effects in particular are difficult to assess. Thus, although surprisingly good linear correlations have been developed between the logarithms of the relative ionization quotients of substituted benzoic acids in aprotic solvents like benzene[20] and the corresponding pK_a values for the acids in water, there is reason to suspect that the influence of the solvent on many substituents is approximately proportional to field effects. At this writing, unfortunately, it has not been possible to unequivocally distinguish between inductive and field effects despite a number of ingenious approaches to the problem.[9] The problem is compounded because the field effect, which is a "through space" interaction of the reactive center with a polar substituent, is sensitive to the dielectric constant of the medium in the *immediate vicinity* of the solute. Completing a vicious circle, the solute-solvent interactions which influence this dielectric constant are themselves dependent on the nature of the solute.

That specific solvent effects do influence the σ values becomes apparent if the solvent dependence of the pK_a values of benzoic acids with strongly polar (OH and NH_2) and weakly polar (CH_3, the halogens) substituents are compared. From such comparisons for the mixed solvents, ethanol-water, the solvent dependence of the σ values for the OH group have been deduced[21] and are listed in Table 4–8. From the trend in the sigma values, it can be seen that the ability of the OH group to stabilize the parent acid relative to the anion apparently increases as the solvating power of the solvent decreases (note that a negative substituent constant implies that the substituted acid is weaker than benzoic acid). The solvent can interact with this solute through general electrostatic forces, the magnitude of which will depend on the dielectric constant, and through specific hydrogen bond formation with either the $—CO_2H$ or the $—OH$ group. In both types of interaction, water should be more effective than ethanol.

In attempting to "explain" this trend of σ values, we should seek an acid-weakening substituent effect which is reduced by solvation. Resonance effects alone cannot provide the answer, because the acid-weakening resonance structures presumed to be important should

---

[20] M. M. Davis and H. B. Hetzler, *J. Res. Natl. Bur. Stand.*, **60,** 569 (1958).
[21] H. H. Jaffe, *Chem. Rev.*, **53,** 191 (1953).

Table 4–8

*Solvent Dependence of the Substituent Constant for the OH
Group of Substituted Benzoic Acids in Ethanol Water Mixtures*

Solvent Composition, Weight Fraction Ethanol	Dielectric Constant of Solvent	Substituent σ^{meta}	Constant[a] σ^{para}
0	88.15	+0.124(+0.121)	−0.328(−0.37)
0.4	55.0	−0.014	−0.285
0.5	49.0	−0.055	−0.335
0.7	38.0	−0.102	−0.350
0.8	32.8	−0.111	−0.384
0.9	28.1	−0.126	−0.414
1.0	24.3	−0.134	−0.442

[a] Derived from ionization constants of substituted benzoic acids.[21]   Values in parentheses based on a more recent evaluation[19].

be enhanced in the more strongly solvating solvents. On the other hand, either a simple inductive or a dipolar field effect can qualitatively account for the trend.

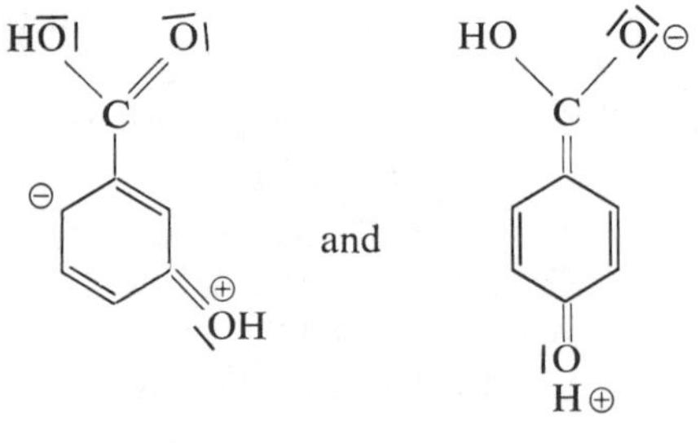

Figure 4–8 Resonance Forms in Substituted Benzoic Acids

In terms of the simple inductive effect, the electronegative OH group becomes negatively charged by the withdrawal of electron density from the ring *via* the sigma bonding framework: the effect strengthens the acid. The capacity of the OH group to accept this charge is increased by interaction with the solvent. Consequently, in the poorer solvents, the simple inductive effect should be less.

The analysis of the field effect can be approached in another way to illustrate the complexity of the problem. On any reasonable scale of electron withdrawing ability we would expect the OH group attached to a phenyl ring to be negatively charged, even with the incorporation of the resonance effects outlined above. The repulsive electrostatic interaction of this group with the negative charge mainly localized on the CO_2^- group of the conjugate base can be reduced by the solvation of the anion. Accordingly, a poorly solvating solvent should destabilize the anion relative to the acid. Qualitative support for either the inductive or field interpretation is obtained when it is noted that the σ^{meta} values are more dependent on the solvent than are the σ^{para}. The resonance effect should be most pronounced for a *para* OH group, whereas the other effects are expected to decrease rapidly as the distance of OH from the reactive center is increased.

A qualitative significance can be ascribed to the ρ values which, as in the case of the substituent constants, defies an unequivocal quantitative analysis: a large positive ρ value for a reaction type indicates that the reaction is facilitated by the withdrawal of electron density from the common reactive center, whereas a large negative ρ value indicates that electron donation facilitates the reaction (recall that the ρ value for the ionization of benzoic acids is $+1$). An inspection of Fig. 4–6 shows, as we would expect, that the ρ values for the ionization of the acids are all positive (a negative ρ value would require a negative slope for a line in that figure). It is of special interest that the ρ values for the ionization of the phenols and anilinium ions are larger than that for the benzoic acid, but the value for the phenylacetic acids is *less*. These results intuitively are reasonable regardless of the origin of the substituent effects. The reactive centers, NH_3^+ and OH, in the former acids are directly attached to the phenyl ring and, consequently should be more sensitive to the substituent effect than the reactive center in phenylacetic acid which is insulated from the ring by a CH_2 and CO group. The quantitative analysis of the ρ values is complicated by the fact that the magnitude, and in a few cases the sign, of ρ is temperature dependent.

To what extent can we justify a correlation of free energy changes with structure? As we have seen in Chapter 3, a ΔH-structure correlation for acid-base reactions in the gas phase seems obvious because we associate ΔH with the strength of the acid-base bond. For these gas phase reactions we implicitly assume that differences in the kinetic energy contributions to ΔH are negligible if structurally similar acids and bases are compared.

The same assumption does *not* apply to acid-base reactions in highly polar solvents, because the strong solute-solvent interactions generally lead to large and variable kinetic energy contributions to ΔH. For example, the ionization of a neutral acid in aqueous solutions is accompanied by the relatively "tight binding" of favorably oriented water molecules to the ions formed (see Figs. 1–2 and 4–2). In this solvation process, a number of water molecules lose kinetic energy of translation and vibration (some, but not all, of this kinetic energy "reappears" in the vibrations of the solvation spheres). The number and orientation of the water molecules, as well as the tightness of binding, is dependent on the charge, size, and shape of the solute ions. Now we would expect that as the solvation energy increases for a series of ions, so would the orientation of the water molecules, *i.e.*, the solvation entropy should become more negative. Indeed for a series of ions of the same general shape, size, and charge—such as the substituted benzoate ions—we might expect the changes in ΔH and ΔS to be proportional. If such is the case, then because of the compensation of the kinetic energy terms in ΔH and ΔS, we can account for the correlation of $\delta \Delta G$ with structural effects (which are largely dependent on internal energy changes). This is the general conclusion which results from a sophisticated treatment[17]—if a series of substituents are to generate a linear free-energy relationship, it is necessary that either they have no effect on the entropy change for the reactions under consideration or that the entropy changes be proportional to the enthalpy changes.

This constraint on the entropy changes generally requires that the substituent be far enough removed from the reactive center so that there are no substantial substituent steric interferences (which contribute to ΔS). For this reason, the *ortho*-substituted phenyl compounds generally do not conform to linear free-energy relationships (compare the data in Table 4–6 with the correlation lines in Fig. 4–6). Similarly, the acidities of the acetic acid derivatives in Table 4–5 do not correlate with those for the phenyl compounds bearing the corresponding *meta*- and *para*-substituents. It is interesting, however, that Taft[22] has been able to derive substituent constants, σ^*, for substituted carboxylic acids by comparing the data for reactions in which steric effects are expected to cancel. These σ^* values, with some exceptions, follow the same *general* trends as the σ^{meta} values.

BASICITIES: ISOELECTRIC REACTIONS

Trends in basicities can, of course, be assessed in terms of the strengths of the conjugate bases of the acids we have discussed in the previous sections. There are two specific comparisons, however, which deserve a more extensive discussion because they shed additional

---

[22] R. W. Taft, *Steric Effects in Organic Chemistry*, ed. by M. S. Newman, John Wiley and Sons, Inc., New York, N.Y. (1956) Chapter 13.

light on the limitations of linear free-energy relationships and on the very important role of specific solvent interactions.

The discussion in the preceding section suggests that contributions from solvent effects might be minimized by comparing data for iso-electric reactions in which the proton is transferred among structurally related bases, *i.e.*

$$C_6H_5CO_2H + XC_6H_4CO_2^{\ominus} \rightleftharpoons XC_6H_4CO_2H + C_6H_5CO_2^{\ominus} \quad \text{(4-8)}$$

or

$$C_6H_5NH_3^+ + XC_6H_4NH_2 \rightleftharpoons XC_6H_4NH_3^+ + C_6H_5NH_2 \quad \text{(4-9)}$$

Indeed, on the basis of a simple electrostatic model,[1,23] the solvent effect should be negligible because the charge is not created or destroyed but merely transferred among species of the same general shape and size. In a sense, this comparison is implicit in the correlation lines of Fig. 4-6, but it is of interest to compare the individual thermodynamic parameters collected in Table 4-9. We must preface our remarks by noting that the range of the appropriate data available is limited, and the accuracy of $\delta \Delta H^0$ and $\delta \Delta S^0$, at best, is 0.1 k. cal. and 0.2 e.u., respectively.

Inspection of the data (incorporating the error limits) reveals that for the benzoic and acetic acids and for the phenols, there is no apparent correlation of $\delta \Delta H^0$ and $\delta \Delta S^0$. This is disturbing, for the benzoic acids and phenols conform to the Hammett relationship and the pK_a values of the substituted acetic acids are a linear function of the Taft σ^* values of the substituents. On the other hand there is, as expected, a smooth (but *not* linear) correlation between the $\delta \Delta H^0$ and $\delta \Delta S^0$ values for the anilinium ions which also conform to a linear free-energy relationship. It is interesting that for the anilinium ions there is an approximately linear correlation between $\delta \Delta G^0$ and $\delta \Delta H^0$.

These data certainly indicate that even in our "best of all possible" models either solvent effects are not completely eliminated or kinetic energy terms involving the solute alone are important.† In addition, the data serve as a graphic reminder that we do *not* know all the

---

[23] W. F. K. Wynne-Jones, *Proc. Roy. Soc.*, **A140**, 440 (1933).

† One such term could be differences in the energy of low frequency bending and deformation vibrations of the anions and parent acids. Whether contributions such as these can produce the effects observed still awaits an unequivocal analysis. Interestingly, it has been found that changes in the frequency of high energy vibrations, such as the OH and CO stretching vibrations in substituted phenols and aldehydes, can be correlated with substituent constants.[24]

[24] C. N. R. Rao and R. Venkataraghavan, *Can. J. Chem.*, **39**, 1757 (1961).

conditions necessary for a *meaningful* linear free-energy relationship to be generated by a series of substituents. A very simple argument will suffice to show that the correlations we discussed in the previous section are not as straightforward as we should like.

The discussion in the preceding section leads us to expect that for the acids in Table 4–9, the substituents generate a linear free-energy relationship because the extra-potential energy changes in ΔH^0 ($\delta \Delta H_{ext}$) are proportional to those changes in ΔS^0 ($\delta \Delta S_{ext}$), *i.e.*

$$\delta \Delta H_{ext} = \beta \delta \Delta S_{ext} \qquad (4\text{--}10)$$

where β is a proportionality constant. But note that, in this model, $\delta \Delta G^0$ will be a measure of the potential energy change induced by the substituent only if the extra-potential energy changes in ΔH^0 and $T \Delta S^0$ *cancel*. This will only occur when β is equal to T, the temperature of the measurement

$$\delta \Delta G^0 = \delta \Delta H^0 - T \Delta S^0 = \delta \Delta H_{int} + \delta \Delta H_{ext} - T \delta \Delta S_{ext}$$
$$= \delta \Delta H_{int} + \delta \Delta H_{ext}(1 - T/\beta) \qquad (4\text{--}11)$$

Referring to equation (4–11), we can see that $\delta \Delta G^0$ will be equal to $\delta \Delta H_{int}$, the potential energy change induced by the substituent (as a first approximation we assume that $\delta \Delta S_{int}$ is negligible), when T/β is one. This puts us in the very difficult position that an observation of a meaningful linear free energy relationship is largely accidental— of all the temperatures and reaction systems available, we must pick those for which $\beta = T$. Equally disturbing is that, even if T/β is one, a *detectable* correlation of the observable quantities $\delta \Delta H^0$ and $\delta \Delta S^0$ will be obtained only if $\delta \Delta H_{ext}$ varies smoothly with $\delta \Delta H_{int}$.

This is only one of a number of possible models[17] for evaluating substituent and solvent effects, but an analysis of each of them leads to the same confusion regarding the *precise* meaning of a linear free-energy relationship and the conditions under which a relationship is liable to be detected. On one point there is no confusion whatsoever. There is a desperate need for a wider variety of *accurate* thermodynamic data obtained at a number of temperatures by calorimetric techniques as well as by the conventional measurements of dissociation constants. It is in a sense disquieting that most of the data available are derived from the latter measurements, into which are built two undesirable features. First, since the evaluation of ΔH^0 is obtained from a plot of $\ln K \, vs. \, 1/T$, it is possible to mask a small, but significant, variation of ΔH^0 with temperature by attributing deviations from a linear plot to experimental error (see also the discussion of the data in Table 4–5). Secondly, unless error limits in $\ln K$ are assessed very carefully, it is possible to generate an *ap-*

Table 4–9

*Thermodynamic Data for Isoelectric Proton Transfer Reactions
(depicted in Equations 4–8 and 4–9) in Water at 25°C**

Acid	$\delta \Delta G^0$ (k. cal. mole^{-1})	$\delta \Delta H^0$ (k. cal. mole^{-1})	$\delta \Delta S^0$ (e.u.)	Reference
BENZOIC	0(+5.74)	0(+0.09)	0(−18.9)	17
meta-methyl	−0.04	+0.02	+0.3	
para-methyl	−0.18	−0.21	0.0	
meta-methoxy	+0.16	+0.03	−0.4	
meta-hydroxy	+0.18	−0.08	−0.8	
para-bromo	+0.28	−0.02	−1.0	
para-chloro	+0.31	−0.14	−1.4	
meta-iodo	+0.48	−0.10	−1.9	
meta-chloro	+0.54	+0.07	−1.5	
meta-bromo	+0.55	+0.15	−1.7	
meta-cyano	+0.83	+0.12	−2.6	
meta-nitro	+1.04	−0.24	−4.4	
ACETIC	0(+6.49)	0(−0.11)	0(−22.1)	1
propionic	−0.16	+0.12	+0.9	
butyric	−0.08	+0.61	+2.3	
formic	+1.38	−0.07	−4.8	
iodoacetic	+2.16	+1.31	−2.8	
bromoacetic	+2.53	+1.13	−4.7	
chloroacetic	+2.58	+1.01	−5.2	
fluoroacetic	+2.96	+1.28	−5.6	
cyanoacetic	+3.12	+0.78	−7.8	
PHENOL	0(+13.67)	0(+5.66)	0(+26.9)	25
meta-methyl	−0.11	+0.14	+0.8	25
para-methyl	+0.35	+0.16	+1.7	25
para-chloro	+0.87	−0.14	−3.4	25
meta-chloro	+1.27	+0.37	−3.1	26
meta-nitro	+2.28	+0.95	−4.4	25
para-nitro	+3.82	+0.95	−10.0	25

* Derived from the thermodynamic data in the references listed, *e.g.*,

$$C_6H_5CO_2H + H_2O \rightleftharpoons C_6H_5CO_2^{\ominus} + H_3O^{\oplus}, \ \Delta H^0$$
$$CH_3C_6H_4CO_2H + H_2O \rightleftharpoons CH_3C_6H_4CO_2^{\ominus} + H_3O^{\oplus}, \ \Delta H_1{}^0$$
$$C_6H_5CO_2H + CH_3C_6H_4CO_2^{\ominus} \rightleftharpoons$$
$$CH_3C_6H_4CO_2H + C_6H_5CO_2^{\ominus}, \ \delta \Delta H^0 = \Delta H^0 - \Delta H_1{}^0$$

Standard values, ΔG^0, ΔH^0, and ΔS^0, for the reference acids are given in parentheses. Note that as $\delta \Delta G^0$ becomes more positive, the proton transfer is *less* favored.

[25] L. G. Hepler, *J. Am. Chem. Soc.*, **85**, 3089 (1963).
[26] W. F. O'Hara and L. G. Hepler, *J. Phys. Chem.*, **65**, 2107 (1961).

Table 4–9 (cont.)

ANILINIUM ION	0(+6.3)	0(+6.8)	0(+1.6)	27
para-methyl	-0.6	0.0	$+1.9$	
meta-methyl	-0.1	$+0.1$	$+0.7$	
para-fluoro	0.0	-0.3	-0.8	
para-chloro	$+0.9$	$+0.5$	-1.4	
para-bromo	$+1.0$	$+0.6$	-1.3	
para-iodo	$+1.1$	$+0.7$	-1.4	
meta-iodo	$+1.4$	$+0.8$	-2.0	
meta-chloro	$+1.5$	$+0.9$	-2.0	
meta-bromo	$+1.5$	$+0.9$	-2.0	
meta-nitro	$+3.0$	$+2.0$	-2.9	
para-nitro	$+5.0$	$+3.7$	-4.3	

parent correlation between ΔH^0 and ΔS^0. Since ΔS^0 is calculated from ΔH^0 into which, of necessity, a larger error is incorporated than in ΔG^0, an error will be incorporated into ΔS^0 of the same magnitude as that in ΔH^0. This is of particular importance in the comparisons of small differences in parameters for structurally related species—it is possible that values of ΔH^0 and ΔS^0 are only a reflection of the imprecision of the temperature coefficients of the ΔG^0 values.*

It should be pointed out that linear free-energy relations are not *solely* a measure of solvent effects. A variety of data is available for systems that do conform to such relations, but for which solvent effects are negligible.[28] Some data which are of interest in terms of the discussion in Chapter 3 are the free energies and enthalpies of association of various phenyl substituted amides ($XC_6H_4C\overset{\displaystyle O}{\diagup}NR_2$) and iodine in carbon tetrachloride.[29] For these adducts the plots of the free energies and enthalpies of association *vs.* the substituent σ parameters are linear. In this system it appears that not only are ΔH^0 and ΔS^0 linearly related, but the values of ΔH_{int} and ΔH_{ext} are proportional.

---

[27] A. I. Biggs, *J. Chem. Soc.*, 2572 (1961). Data for 30°C.

* A similar analysis of enthalpy-entropy and linear free energy relationships for reaction rates has been provided by R. C. Petersen, *J. Org. Chem.*, **29**, 3133 (1964).

[28] For example see the interesting correlation developed by Taft et al. between σ parameters and the ^{19}F chemical shifts of benzene derivatives in a variety of solvents. R. W. Taft et al., *J. Am. Chem. Soc.*, **85**, 709 (1963).

[29] R. L. Carson and R. S. Drago, *J. Am. Chem. Soc.*, **85**, 505 (1963).

Despite our uncertainty about the interpretation of the thermodynamic data obtained in a single solvent, a *limited* qualitative correlation of solvent effects on isoelectric reactions is possible. Simple electrostatic theory[1,23] requires that values of ΔG^0 for these reactions be proportional to $1/\epsilon$, where ϵ is the dielectric constant of the medium. For closely related acid-base pairs, (*e.g.*, benzoic acid-*meta*-bromobenzoate ion or anilinium ion—*meta*-nitroaniline) in the highly polar solvents water, methanol, and ethanol, it has been found that ΔG^0 *is* a linear function of $1/\epsilon$. But once again the intervention of specific solvent effects is indicated by the systems which deviate from the correlation. Thus, the equilibria in formamide, which in terms of dielectric constant ($\epsilon = 111.5$ at 25°C) is even more polar than water ($\epsilon = 80.4$ at 25°C), do not conform to the linear correlation. Similarly, neither do the equilibria in the solvent *n*-butanol ($\epsilon = 17.5$) which is only slightly less polar than ethanol ($\epsilon = 24.2$ at 25°C). One is left with the suspicion that the correlation between $\delta \Delta G^0$ and $1/\epsilon$ is only an indication of the extent to which the alcohols above resemble water in their solvent properties.

It must be remembered that water (and to a lesser extent, an alcohol) is a highly structured liquid consisting of hydrogen-bonded clusters of solvent molecules. The introduction of a solute involves not only general electrostatic interactions but also specific hydrogen bond formation and interactions which enhance or disrupt the structure of the clusters. To the extent that solutes differ in their hydrogen-bonding capabilities and in their effect on the structure of water, the simple electrostatic model will fail. For similar reasons, the model will *not* be appropriate for comparing equilibria in solvents whose structures differ markedly. An illustration of the importance of these considerations is provided by a comparison of the dissociation constants of the tetraalkylammonium halide ion pairs, $R_4N^+X^-$, in hydroxylic and nonhydroxylic solvents.[30]

As expected in terms of the simple electrostatic theory, the dissociation constants of the tetraalkylammonium halide ion pairs in solvents such as acetone ($\epsilon = 20.47$) and acetonitrile ($\epsilon = 36.09$) *increase* as the size of the anion *increases*. On the other hand, for a hydroxylic solvent such as methanol ($\epsilon = 32.62$), the dissociation constants *decrease* as the size of the anion *increases*. Indeed, whereas tetrabutylammonium iodide is completely dissociated in dilute acetonitrile solutions, the concentration of the ion-pair is measurable

---

[30] R. L. Kay and D. Fennell Evans, *J. Phys. Chem.*, **69**, 4216 (1965) and references therein.

in methanol and even water. It is significant that, in contradistinction to water and methanol, nonhydroxylic solvents such as acetone and acetonitrile are relatively structureless, the solvent-solvent interactions being weakly dipolar. This remarkable behavior of large cations and anions in hydroxylic solvents is attributed[31] to the "structure-breaking" effects. In effect, large ions of small charge are hydrophobic in that they "weaken" the water (or methanol) structure by deforming or straining the hydrogen bonds and then cannot compensate for this effect through a strong solute-solvent attraction. Water resists this deformation by "pushing" the ions together to form the ion-pair, thereby minimizing the water-solute interaction and decreasing the electrostatic free energy of the system. The effect that solutes have on the structure of water can also have a pronounced effect on the measured entropy values. This effect has too often been ignored. H. S. Frank[32] has proposed that liquid water consists of clumps, with an ice like structure, that are constantly breaking and forming. The addition of a nonpolar solute, e.g., argon, isolates a given unit so it is less susceptible to perturbations by other water molecules. Addition of nonpolar solutes also tend to constrain certain water molecules to a given volume making the water more susceptible to association. Consequently, the solvent becomes more highly ordered giving rise to a negative entropy contribution. The importance of these solvent effects as they relate specifically to trends in basicities is discussed next.

RELATIVE BASICITIES OF AMINES

The thermodynamic data for the dissociation of some representative ammonium ions in water are collected in Table 4–10. A comparison of the statistically corrected standard free energies of dissociation reveals the surprising order for increasing basicity of the parent amines, $NH_3 < (CH_3)_3N < (CH_3)_2NH < CH_3NH_2 < (C_2H_5)_3N < (C_2H_5)_2NH$. If the free energies of dissociation were solely a measure of the relative donor strengths of the amines we would expect a correlation with the E and C numbers (or some combination thereof) reported in Chapter 3. Recall that the donor strength toward iodine and phenol could be correlated. Studies[33] of the proton affinities indicates that the donor strength of these amines toward the proton in the gas phase *does* increase in accordance with

[31] R. M. Diamond, *J. Phys. Chem.*, **67**, 2513 (1963).

[32] H. S. Frank and W. Wen *Discussions Faraday Soc.*, **24**, 133–40 (1957). See also other articles by Professor Frank listed in Chemical Abstracts.

[33] M. S. B. Munson, *J. Am. Chem. Soc.*, **87**, 2332 (1965).

Table 4–10

Thermodynamic Data for the Ionization of Alkylammonium Ions in Water at 25°C[a]

Acid	ΔG^0	ΔH^0	ΔS^0	Reference	$\Delta G_1{}^0$	$\Delta S_1{}^0$
$NH_4{}^+$	+12.67	+12.43	−0.8	35	+13.50	−3.6
$CH_3NH_3{}^+$	14.48	13.09	−4.7	36	15.15	−6.9
$C_2H_5NH_3{}^+$	14.55	13.58	−3.1	37	15.16	−5.3
$n\text{-}C_3H_7NH_3{}^+$	14.39	13.85	−1.7	37	15.01	−3.9
$n\text{-}C_4H_9NH_3{}^+$	14.48	14.07	−1.3	37	15.11	−3.5
$(CH_3)_2NH_2{}^+$	14.42	11.88	−9.5	36	15.13	−10.9
$(C_2H_5)_2NH_2{}^+$	15.02	12.77	−7.2	37	15.33	−8.6
$(CH_3)_3NH^+$	13.36	8.86	−15.1	35	13.66	−15.1
$(C_2H_5)_3NH^+$	14.66	10.38	−14.4	35	14.66	−14.4

[a] ΔG^0, ΔH^0, and ΔS^0 are experimental values in k. cal. mole^{-1}, k. cal. mole.$^{-1}$, and cal. deg.$^{-1}$ mole.$^{-1}$, respectively. Values of $\Delta G_1{}^0$ and $\Delta S_1{}^0$ are the experimental values corrected for statistical effects. The statistical effect arises because, apart from any bonding considerations, it is four times as probable that a proton will dissociate from $NH_4{}^+$ than from $(CH_3)_3NH^+$ or $(C_2H_5)_3NH^+$. In the former there are four equivalent dissociable protons but in the latter two only one. Consequently the data, to be meaningful in structural terms, must be normalized to the number of equivalent dissociable protons. Thus for $NH_4{}^+$, the dissociation constant per proton is $K_{observed} \div 4$ and for $(CH_3)RNH_3{}^+$ it is $K_{observed} \div 3$. The procedure for correcting for these statistical effects in a variety of systems is outlined by Benson.[38] It is to be noted that these statistical corrections for the other species which participate in the equilibria can be neglected. The parent amines each have only one coordination site (the lone pair of electrons) to accept the proton; and water is the reference base common to all these reactions. Since the statistical correction is temperature independent, only ΔS and ΔG (*not* ΔH) are affected.

the inductive effect, *i.e.*, it parallels the *C* numbers. Accordingly, some solvent effect must be operative in producing this "anomalous" order of basicities.

That solvent effects are of primary importance in determining the basicities of this series of amines is also evident in the work of Pearson and Vogelsong,[34] who studied the solvent dependence of the equilibrium constants for the reactions of amines with 2,4-dinitrophenol

[34] R. G. Pearson and D. C. Vogelsong, *J. Am, Chem. Soc.*, **80**, 1038 (1958).

[35] P. Paoletti, J. H. Stern, and A. Vacca, *J. Phys. Chem.*, **69**, 3759 (1965).

[36] D. H. Everett and W. F. K. Wynne-Jones, *Trans. Faraday Soc.*, **35**, 1380 (1939).

[37] A. G. Evans and S. D. Hamann, *Trans. Faraday Soc.*, **47**, 34 (1951).

[38] S. W. Benson, *J. Am. Chem. Soc.*, **80**, 5151 (1958).

Table 4-11

Equilibrium Constants as a Function of Solvent for the Reaction of Amines with 2,4-Dinitrophenol at 25°C

Base	Benzene ($\epsilon = 2.3$)	Dioxane ($\epsilon = 2.2$)	Equilibrium Constant[a] Chloroform ($\epsilon = 4.8$)	Chloro-benzene ($\epsilon = 5.6$)	Ethyl acetate ($\epsilon = 6.3$)
CH_3NH_2	—	4800 (18,400)	35 (105)	—	—
$(CH_3)_2NH$	880 (1760)	5410 (10,820)	1230 (2460)	1070 (2140)	—
$(CH_3)_3N$	802 (802)	382 (382)	2680 (2680)	1380 (1380)	—
$(C_2H_5)NH_2$	—	4900 (14,700)	—	—	65,500 (196,500)
$(C_2H_5)_2NH$	1240 (2480)	6230 (12,460)	1730 (3460)	2500 (5000)	47,500 (95,000)
$(C_2H_5)_3N$	2940 (2940)	1460 (1,460)	15,800 (15,800)	9680 (9680)	11,900 (11,900)
$(n\text{-}C_4H_9)NH_2$	—	3760 (11,280)	45 (135)	—	38,100 (114,300)
$(n\text{-}C_4H_9)_2NH$	950 (1900)	4010 (8,020)	2580 (5160)	2500 (5000)	36,000 (72,000)
$(n\text{-}C_4H_9)_3N$	614 (614)	420 (425)	9100 (9100)	3800 (3800)	2520 (2520)

[a] Experimental data[34] statistically corrected values in parenthesis (*cf.* Table 4-11). ϵ is the solvent dielectric constant at 25°C.

(equation 4–12)

$$R_3N + HOC_6H_3(NO_2)_2 \rightleftharpoons [R_3NH^+OC_6H_3(NO_2)_2{}^-] \quad \textbf{(4-12)}$$

The data obtained are collected in Table 4–11. There is some uncertainty about the quantitative interpretation of the equilibrium constants for the individual reactions because the product in each case is the ion pair (note that all the solvents listed in the table have very low dielectric constants) for which some dissociation is expected, especially in the more basic solvents (dioxane and ethyl acetate). The trends in the equilibrium constants, however, can readily be interpreted qualitatively.

For the solvents incapable of forming hydrogen bonds to the ammonium ions (benzene, chloroform, and chlorobenzene), the equilibrium constants indicate that the basicities of the amines are either very similar or follow the trend in the inductive effect, $R_3N > R_2NH > RNH_2$. In the solvents dioxane and ethyl acetate, however, the basicities of the amines are strongly differentiated (the relative values of the equilibrium constants are much larger than those for the other solvents), and follow the trend, not of the inductive effect, but of a steric effect, $RNH_2 > R_2NH \gg R_3N$. Since ethyl acetate and dioxane are bulky molecules capable of forming relatively strong hydrogen bonds to the ammonium ions, this trend is the "expected" one if specific solvation of the cations occurs. Both in terms of steric effects and the number of hydrogen bonds that can be formed, the trend of increasing cation-solvent interaction should be $RNH_3{}^+ > R_2NH_2{}^+ > R_3NH^+$ (we have neglected the weaker interactions of the uncharged amines and acids).

Specific solvent effects should be even more important for the ionization of these amines in water. It is now generally accepted that the "formula" of the hydrated proton in water is $H_9O_4{}^+$ (see Fig. 1–2), and that for the hydrated ammonium ion it is probably $NH_4{}^+(OH_2)_4$ (see Fig. 4–9). The evidence for the existence of the hydrated hydronium ion has been obtained from a variety of studies of aqueous solutions, one of which we will discuss in the next section. The existence of the hydrated ammonium ion is inferred from the similarities in size and hydrogen bonding capabilities of H_3O^+ and $NH_4{}^+$. *Direct* evidence for the existence of these solvated species in the gas phase has recently become available from the studies of the mass spectrum of the proton in the presence of water and ammonia vapor. The predominant ions detected[39] in the mass spectrum of the proton in water vapor are H_3O^+, $H_5O_2{}^+$, $H_7O_3{}^+$ and $H_9O_4{}^+$. From

---

[39] P. F. Knewstubb and A. W. Tickner, *J. Chem. Phys.*, **38**, 464 (1964) and references therein.

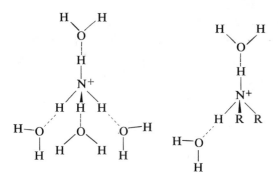

Figure 4–9 Probable Structures for Aquation of Ammonium and Dialkylammonium Ions.

the dependence of the ion distribution on the partial pressure of water vapor, it can be concluded that the binding energy between the H_3O^+ and n additional water molecules decreases slowly as n increases, up to $n = 3(H_9O_4^+)$, but it decreases drastically for $n > 3$. Similarly the mass spectrum of the proton in ammonia and ammonia-water vapor indicates that the ions, $NH_4^+(n\,NH_3)$ and $NH_4^+(n\,H_2O)$, have large binding energies (per mole of NH_3 or H_2O) for values of n, $1 \leq n \leq 4$, but the binding energy decreases markedly for $n > 4$.[40]

Consequently, there is some justification for explicitly incorporating the effects of specific solvation in the ionization of the ammonium ions in water as indicated in the equations for the reactions

$$NH_4^+(4\,H_2O) + H_2O_{(aq)} \rightleftharpoons NH_{3(aq)} + H_3O^+(3\,H_2O) + H_2O_{(aq)}$$

$$\text{(4–13a)}$$

$$RNH_3^+(3\,H_2O) + H_2O_{(aq)} \rightleftharpoons RNH_{2(aq)} + H_3O^+(3\,H_2O) \quad \text{(4–13b)}$$

$$R_2NH_2^+(2\,H_2O) + 2\,H_2O \rightleftharpoons R_2NH_{(aq)} + H_3O^+(3\,H_2O) \quad \text{(4–13c)}$$

$$R_3NH^+(H_2O) + 3\,H_2O \rightleftharpoons R_3N_{(aq)} + H_3O^+(3\,H_2O) \quad \text{(4–13d)}$$

On the basis of these reactions we can qualitatively account for many features of the data listed in Table 4–10. For the sake of brevity, the solvation of water and the parent amines (and the secondary solvation of the ions) is not discussed, but it should be recognized that these effects can be important, especially in the comparison of small differences in the thermodynamic parameters.

---

[40] A. M. Hogg, R. M. Haynes, and P. Kebarle, *J. Am. Chem. Soc.*, **88**, 28 (1966) and references therein.

First we should expect, and do observe (Table 4–10), the *largest* decrease in entropy for the ionization of the trialkylammonium ions and the *smallest* relative decrease for the ionization of the ammonium ion. In the former reaction, the product ion, H_3O^+, effectively "immobilizes" three water molecules in the primary hydration sphere, but the reactant, only one molecule. This loss in the translational and rotational freedom of two solvated water molecules should be reflected in a large negative entropy change for the reaction. Similarly, the decrease in entropy accompanying the reaction depicted in equation (4–13a) should be small, since one water molecule actually "escapes" the constrictive influence of the primary hydration spheres of the ions (note that we have neglected the entropy change associated with the formation of H_3O^+ itself and the "destruction" of NH_4^+).

The influence of specific solvation is also apparent in the relative values of ΔH^0. The enthalpy changes accompanying the ionization of the di- and tri-alkylammonium ions are, in general, less unfavorable than those for the ionization reactions of the other ammonium ions. For the former, heat should be released due to the incorporation of additional water molecules into the primary hydration sphere of the product (H_3O^+) relative to the reactant ion. For the other ammonium ions, this solvation enthalpy effect is either absent or unfavorable.

The differences among the thermodynamic parameters for a given series of alkylammonium ions (*e.g.*, the series RNH_3^+) are too small to warrant an extensive discussion here. However, it is interesting that Condon,[41] by "correcting" the free energies of ionization of a wide variety of substituted ammonium ions for statistical and specific solvation effects, has obtained an acceptable correlation between the basicity of an amine and the inductive effect of the substituents (measured by the Taft inductive parameters, σ^*).

PROTON TRANSFER REACTIONS IN HIGHLY ACIDIC SOLUTIONS

Some very interesting findings, particularly in organic chemistry, have developed from studies in highly acidic solvents. In these solvents, the equilibrium concentrations of ions are large and the activities of the acid and base are much different from one. We will restrict our attention to the sulfuric acid solvent system, in which the widest range of quantitative studies has been completed, but our

---

[41] F. E. Condon, *J. Am. Chem. Soc.*, **87**, 4481–4496 (1965).

comments apply equally well to other highly acidic systems (*e.g.*, HCl, HNO_3, and HF).

Before discussing the quantitative aspects of the equilibria it is appropriate to survey some of the common reactions which occur in concentrated sulfuric acid. Sulfuric acid-water solutions are excellent conductors of electricity. Studies of the freezing points of these solutions, in conjunction with the conductivity studies, indicate that the following reactions occur (only a few of those possible are depicted) in these solutions

$$H_2SO_4 + H_2O \rightleftharpoons H_3O^+ + HSO_4^- \qquad \text{(4-14)}$$

$$2\,H_2SO_4 \rightleftharpoons H_3SO_4^+ + HSO_4^- \qquad \text{(4-15)}$$

$$H_3SO_4^+ + SO_4^{2-} \rightleftharpoons H_3O^+ + S_2O_7^{2-} \qquad \text{(4-16)}$$

In dilute and moderately concentrated aqueous sulfuric acid, reaction 4–14 is the most important and proceeds essentially to completion. In concentrated sulfuric acid or fuming sulfuric acid, reactions 4–15 and 4–16 are the most important ones.* The occurrence of these reactions is responsible for two important properties of the solvent system: the very high activity of the proton and the very low activity of water.

The very high proton activities of these systems lead to interesting protonation equilibria. It will be recalled that the "strong" acids, $HClO_4$, HNO_3, and HBr, are leveled to the same *apparent* acidity in the basic solvent water. In 100% sulfuric acid, however, the ClO_4^- ion is converted to $HClO_4$.[42] In solutions of lower proton activity, the nitrate ion is partially converted to HNO_3 (in 44% H_2SO_4)[43] and preliminary data suggest[44] that the Br^- ion is partially converted to HBr in 70–80% H_2SO_4. These protonation equilibria imply either the following sequence of increasing acidity, $HBr < HNO_3 < HClO_4$, or of decreasing basicity of the conjugate bases, $Br^- > NO_3^- > ClO_4^-$.

The very low water activities in these systems allow reactions to proceed which will not occur to a significant extent in water. The following reactions, in which the very reactive NO_2^+ and NO^+ ions are

---

* Fuming sulfuric acid is a solution of SO_3 in H_2SO_4. Note that "hydrated" SO_3 is H_2OSO_3 and that $H_3OSO_3^+$ can dissociate into H_3O^+ and SO_3. The SO_3, in turn, can react with SO_4^{2-} to form $S_2O_7^{2-}$.

[42] R. J. Gillespie, *J. Chem. Soc.*, 2537 (1950).
[43] N. C. Deno, *J. Phys. Chem.*, **65**, 199 (1961).
[44] N. Deno, private communication.

formed, proceed essentially to completion in concentrated H_2SO_4.[45]

$$HNO_3 + 2\,H_2SO_4 \rightleftharpoons NO_2^+ + H_3O^+ + 2\,HSO_4^- \qquad \text{(4–17)}$$

$$HNO_2 + 2\,H_2SO_4 \rightleftharpoons NO^+ + H_3O^+ + 2\,HSO_4^- \qquad \text{(4–18)}$$

These reactions can *formally* be considered to be the abstraction of the OH^- ion by the highly acidic solvent. Similar reactions occur with selected organic alcohols to form reactive carbonium ions.[46]

$$(C_6H_5)_3COH + 2H^+ \underset{H_2SO_4}{\overset{50\%}{\rightleftharpoons}} (C_6H_5)_3C^+ + H_3O^+$$

Considering the variety of chemistry that is accessible in highly acidic solvents, it is important to explore the quantitative aspects of the equilibria obtained in these systems. Such an exploration is also of interest because the proton transfer reactions of very weak bases can be studied only in highly acidic solvents. In view of the complexity of these solvents, it will be necessary to place a good deal of reliance upon simple structural models for the proton transfer reactions. In this discussion our attention is focused not on the bases but on the proton-donating ability of the solvent.

The simplest analysis of the proton-donating abilities of highly acidic solvents is through the use of acidity functions first introduced by Hammett and Deyrup.[47,48] If a *small* amount of an uncharged reference base, B, is added to an acidic solvent, a simple measure of the proton donating ability of the solvent is the ratio of the concentration of the conjugate acid, $[BH^+]$, to that of the base present at equilibrium. Alternatively, we can "factor out" the basicity of the reference base by incorporating the dissociation constant of the conjugate acid, K_{BH^+}

$$BH^+ \rightleftharpoons B + H^+ \qquad \text{(4–19)}$$

By means of this reaction we can define the quantities h_0 and H_0 using equations 4–20 and 4–21.

$$h_0 \equiv K_{BH} + \frac{[BH^+]}{[B]} \qquad \text{(4–20)}$$

$$H_0 \equiv -\log h_0 = pK_{BH} + -\log \frac{[BH^+]}{[B]} \qquad \text{(4–21)}$$

---

[45] R. J. Gillespie and J. Graham, *J. Chem. Soc.*, 2532 (1952) and references therein.

[46] N. C. Deno, P. T. Groves, J. Jaruzelski, and M. Lugasch, *J. Am. Chem. Soc.*, **82**, 4719 (1960) and references therein.

[47] L. P. Hammett and A. J. Deyrup, *J. Am. Chem. Soc.*, **54**, 2721 (1932).

[48] M. A. Long and F. A. Long, *Chem. Rev.*, **57**, 1 (1957).

These definitions may seem trivial because H_0, called the *acidity function* of the solvent, and h_0 are equal to the pH and [H$^+$], respectively, of *solutions of very dilute aqueous acids*. However, conditions are far from ideal in concentrated acid solutions, and for these systems the acidity function acquires a special meaning.

In the usual manner, these deviations from ideality can be "corrected" by incorporating activities and activity coefficients into equation 4–21, which after some algebraic manipulation becomes

$$H_0 = -\log a_{H^+} + \log \gamma_{BH^+}/\gamma_B \qquad (4\text{–}22)$$

[Recall that K_{BH^+} is $a_{BH^+}/a_B a_{H^+} = [BH^+]/[B][H^+] \times (\gamma_{BH^+}/\gamma_B \gamma_{H^+})$]. The acidity function, defined by equation 4–22, should be independent of the reference base B. However equation 4–22 is not very useful for our purposes, since it contains two terms which cannot be directly evaluated—the single ion activity, a_{H^+}, and the activity coefficient, γ_{BH^+}. All the terms in equation 4–21, on the other hand, correspond to measureable quantities. The pK_{BH^+} values are obtained from conventional studies of dilute acidic solutions (or from an extrapolation to dilute solution conditions, of data obtained in concentrated acid solutions) of the reference base B or its conjugate acid BH$^+$. The ratio [BH$^+$]/[B] is usually evaluated from spectrophotometric measurements (see Chapter 3) using indicator bases such as the colored nitroanilines, the conjugate acids of which are colorless.

The usefulness of the acidity function so obtained (from equation 4–22) depends upon the fact that its value is approximately independent of the uncharged reference base B. Since "dilute solution" pK values are used in that equation, for the uncharged bases, B, $B_1, \ldots, B_n$, the following relationship is valid for a given solvent

$$\log \frac{\gamma_{BH^+}}{\gamma_B} = \log \frac{\gamma_{B_1H^+}}{\gamma_{B_1}} = \cdots = \log \frac{\gamma_{B_nH^+}}{\gamma_{B_n}} \qquad (4\text{–}23)$$

Considering our previous discussion of solute-solvent interactions, this relationship certainly is expected to apply to structurally related bases. In practice, the H_0 values are found to correlate the rates and equilibria[48] for the reactions of many uncharged bases.

Consequently, at least as a first approximation, the H_0 values can be interpreted in terms of equation (4–22) as a measure of the proton activity of a solvent. It is expected that the term $\log \gamma_{BH^+}/\gamma_B$ makes a much smaller contribution to H_0 than the $\log a_{H^+}$ term, especially at the higher acid concentrations. In turn, the activity, or thermodynamic concentration, of the proton in a given solvent should be a sensitive measure of the relative ability of that solvent to donate a proton to a base.

This conclusion follows from the fact that the free energy of the proton in a given solvent, $\overline{G}_{H^+}$, can be expressed as a function of its free energy in the standard state, $\overline{G}_{H^+}{}^0$, and of its activity in the solvent

$$\overline{G}_{H^+} = \overline{G}_{H^+}{}^0 + RT \ln a_{H^+} \qquad (4\text{--}24)$$

Now the free energy change, $\Delta\overline{G}$, for the reaction $B + H^+ \rightleftharpoons BH^+$ is given by $\Delta\overline{G} = \overline{G}_{BH^+} - \overline{G}_B - \overline{G}_{H^+}$. For a given base (neglecting changes in a_{BH^+} and a_B as a function of the solvent), the latter equation implies that the larger is the proton activity, the more positive is $\overline{G}_{H^+}$ and the more negative is $\Delta\overline{G}$. That is to say, the larger is a_{H^+}, the more the proton transfer reaction will proceed to the right.

In Table 4–12 are collected selected H_0 values for representative acidic solvents. As expected, the H_0 values or the proton-donating abilities of each of these solvents increase markedly as the concentration of the acid in the aqueous solutions increases. Indeed, at first glance, the H_0 values at the higher acid concentrations seem impossibly large. Thus the H_0 value for 70% perchloric acid implies that the proton activity is of the order 10^{+7} (as a first approximation we neglect the term $\log \gamma_{BH^+}/\gamma_B$ in equation 4–23). Since the *formal* molality of the proton in 70% perchloric acid is only $10^{1.37}$, this

Table 4–12

Selected Values of Acidity Functions (25°C) for Aqueous Acids[a]

	$-H_0$			
Wt. $-$ % Acid	H_2SO_4[b]	$HClO_4$	HNO_3	HCl
5.	-0.24 (0)	-0.20	-0.03	0.42
10.	0.31 (0.025)	0.19	0.39	1.00
20.	1.01 (0.06)	0.90	0.95	2.12
30.	1.72 (0.12)	1.53	1.42	3.51
40.	2.41 (0.25)	2.55	1.77	
50.	3.38 (0.46)	3.64		
60.	4.46 (0.79)	5.20		
70.	5.65 (1.34)	7.87		
80.	6.97 (2.26)			
90.	8.27 (3.61)			
95.	8.86 (4.40)			
100.	11.10			

[a] Taken from collection in reference 48.
[b] Values in parentheses are $-\log a_{H_2O}$ (a_{H_2O} = activity of water).

value of a_{H^+} requires a proton activity coefficient of $10^{+5.63}$. In terms of the discussion in Chapter 2, how can we rationalize an activity coefficient which not only is *larger than one* but is so much larger?

The explanation, of course, involves our choice of standard states. The standard state selected for the proton ($a_{H^+} = 1$) in these systems is the "infinitely dilute" aqueous solution for which the ion-ion distances are very large and for which there is a very large excess of water available to solvate the ions. For the standard state then, $RT \ln a_{H^+} = 0$ and $\overline{G}_{H^+} = \overline{G}_{H^+}{}^0$. If the dilute acidic solution is progressively concentrated, the mean proton-anion distances decrease and so must the electrostatic free energy of the proton (due to the increased proton-anion interaction). Since the standard free energy is taken to be constant, the decrease in the free energy of the proton, $\overline{G}_{H^+}$, must be reflected in a lower a_{H^+} (see equation 4–24). However the concentration process at some stage must eventually lead to an *increase* in the free energy of the proton (and consequently an increase in a_{H^+} and γ_{H^+}) because the amount of water available to solvate the ions is progressively decreasing. In addition, in the more concentrated solutions the proton-proton and anion-anion repulsions become important.

Accordingly, the activity of the proton in 70% $HClO_4$ does not seem unreasonably large if it is recognized that in the solution only 1.4 moles of water are available to solvate one mole of H_3O^+ and one mole of ClO_4^- ion. There is not enough water available even to complete the primary hydration sphere of *one* of the ions.

These same effects are reflected in the trends in the water activities— as the acid concentration increases the free energy of water per mole decreases because of ion-water interactions. For example, the value of a_{H_2O} in 80% H_2SO_4 is only $10^{-2.26}$. In the light of the discussion in previous sections, it is interesting that Bascombe and Bell[49,50] have shown that H_0 values of sulfuric acid can be calculated, at least in the concentration range $0\% \leq H_2SO_4 \leq 50\%$, by assuming that the proton exists as the species $H_9O_4^+$. The large decrease in a_{H_2O} and the large increase in a_{H^+} for solutions in which the concentration of H_2SO_4 is greater than 50% can be attributed to the fact that the ion $H_9O_4^+$ cannot be completely formed because there is an insufficient amount of water.

---

[49] Bascombe and R. P. Bell, *Disc. Faraday Soc.*, **24**, 158 (1957).

[50] R. P. Bell, *The Proton in Chemistry*, Chapter 2, Cornell University Press, Ithaca, N.Y. (1959).

It should be pointed out that although H_0 may be principally a measure of $\log a_{H^+}$, the term $\log(\gamma_{BH^+}/\gamma_B)$ in equation 4–23 probably increases rapidly as the acid concentration increases. The free energies (and consequently the activity coefficients) of BH^+ and B should be a relatively sensitive function of specific solvent (hydrogen-bonding) interactions. For acidic solvents, there is a certain symmetry in these interactions which involve the hydrogen bonding of BH^+

with a water molecule $BH^+{\cdots}O\begin{smallmatrix}\nearrow H\\\searrow H\end{smallmatrix}$, and of B with a hydronium ion

$B{\cdots}H{-}O\begin{smallmatrix}\nearrow H+\\\searrow H\end{smallmatrix}$. The two adducts are introconvertible *via* a simple

proton shift. Nonetheless, the free energies of the two adducts are affected differently by changes in the solvent composition. As the acid concentration is increased, the free energy and activity coefficient of BH^+ would be expected to rise rapidly because the water concentration (or activity) is decreasing, whereas the free energy and activity coefficient of B would be expected to decrease because the concentration of the H_3O^+ ion is increasing. Thus for the H_0 values to correlate the equilibria successfully in a given set of reactions, not only must the structural changes which occur be similar to those pertaining to the protonation equilibria for the reference base but the nature of the solute-solvent interactions must also be analogous.

METAL IONS IN WATER

Metal ions of high charge and small ionic radius undergo hydrolysis reactions in water which can be represented by

$$M^{n+}_{(aq)} + HOH_{(aq)} \rightleftharpoons MOH_{(aq)}^{(n-1)+} + H_{(aq)}^+ \tag{4–25}$$

$$[M(OH_2)_x]_{(aq)}^{n+} \rightleftharpoons [M(OH_2)_{x-1}OH]_{(aq)}^{(n-1)+} + H_{(aq)}^+ \tag{4–26}$$

The hydrolysis constants, K_h, [equilibrium constants for reaction 4–25 or 4–26] for selected metal ions in "infinitely dilute" aqueous solutions are collected in Table 4–13. In attempting to relate the hydrolysis constants to the "inherent" properties of the metal ion, we are faced with the same difficulties encountered in the previous sections of this chapter.

The simplest correlation of these equilibria involves the electro-static approach. In terms of equation 4–25, it can be argued that those metal ions of the highest charge and the smallest radius will exhibit the largest affinity for the hydroxide ion. Consequently they should exhibit the largest hydrolysis constants (or the smallest pK_h values). Alternatively, in terms of equation 4–26, it can be argued that the ions of small radius and high charge facilitate the dissociation of the proton because they cause the greatest polarization of the water molecules.

An inspection of the table reveals that, with some important exceptions, the data conform to the gross trend expected on the basis of these electrostatic arguments. Large, and perhaps significant, deviations from the expected trend are exhibited by Hg^{2+} (especially with respect to the pK_h value for Zn^{2+}), Sn^{2+}, Pb^{2+}, and In^{3+} (especially with respect to Al^{3+}). There are not sufficient thermo-

Table 4–13

Hydrolysis Constants for Selected Metal Ions at 25°C[a]

Ion	$-\log K_h (pK_h)$	$r^{[b]}$
Li^+	13.8	0.60
Na^+	14.7	0.95
Ag^+	11.7	1.26
Be^{2+}	3.6	0.31
Mg^{2+}	11.4	0.65
Ca^{2+}	12.7	0.99
Co^{2+}	12.2	0.74
Ni^{2+}	10.6	0.72
Zn^{2+}	9.7	0.74
Hg^{2+}	2.5	1.10
Sn^{2+}	1.7	1.12
Pb^{2+}	7.8[d]	1.20
V^{3+}	2.9[c]	0.74
Cr^{3+}	3.9	0.69
Fe^{3+}	2.2	0.64
Al^{3+}	5.0	0.50
In^{3+}	3.7[c]	0.81

[a] Values taken from, "Stability Constants," *Special Publication No. 7*, Chemical Society (London), Part II.

[b] Empirical crystallographic ionic radii, in Å, taken from, L. Pauling, "Nature of the Chemical Bond," Cornell University Press, 3rd Ed., Ithaca, N.Y., 1960.

[c] Value obtained in dilute solution but not corrected, or extrapolated, to "infinitely dilute" conditions.

[d] Value obtained at 18°C.

dynamic data (particularly the appropriate ΔH^0 and ΔS^0 values) available at present to warrant a discussion of the "reasons" for these deviations (*e.g.*, in terms of "covalence" in the M^{n+}—OH^- interaction). Instead, it is of interest to devote the remaining portion of this section to an outline of the structural ambiguities inherent in the processes represented by equations 4–25 and 4–26.

Although the appropriate direct experimental observations are limited, it is generally accepted that most metal ions not only exist as hydrated species in aqueous solutions but form metal ion-water complexes of well-defined structure. The classical demonstration of the existence of a well defined aquometal ion complex in aqueous solution was provided by Hunt and Taube[51] who showed that water, enriched or "labeled" with the oxygen isotope of mass 18,* exchanges very slowly with the water in the first coordination sphere of Cr(III) (see equation 4–27). In simple terms, their *isotope dilution* experiment involved

$$Cr(^{16}OH_2)_n{}^{3+} + x\,^{18}OH_2 \rightleftharpoons Cr(^{18}OH_2)_n{}^{3+} + x\,^{16}OH_2 \quad \textbf{(4–27)}$$

mixing a fixed amount of ^{18}O enriched water with a fixed amount of normal Cr(III) perchlorate solution of known composition. All of the water in the latter, except the n molecules tightly bonded in the first coordination sphere of Cr(III), immediately mixed with and diluted the ^{18}O enriched water in the former. Further dilution of the resulting ^{18}O enriched solution then occurred slowly *via* the reaction shown in 4–27. Sampling the solvent by means of distillations, Hunt and Taube[51] were able to calculate both the rate of isotope (and hence water) exchange between the "bulk" solvent and the primary coordination number, n. The primary coordination obtained, six, is consistent with the octahedral coordination of six water molecules deduced from the study of the electronic absorption spectrum of Cr(III) in aqueous solutions. An extension of these studies to solutions of aluminum perchlorate showed that the primary solvation number of Al(III) in water is also six[52] [again, presumably involving the coordination of the water molecules at the apices of a regular octahedron about the Al(III) ion].

Nuclear magnetic resonance (NMR) spectroscopy has also been used to show that the Be^{2+} ion in water coordinates to four water

[51] J. P. Hunt and H. Taube, *J. Chem. Phys.*, **19**, 602 (1951).

* The oxygen in water from natural sources consists approximately of 99.78% of mass number 16, 0.02% of mass number 17, and 0.2% of mass 18.

[52] H. Baldwin and H. Taube, *J. Chem. Phys.*, **33**, 206 (1960).

molecules in its primary hydration sphere[53] (presumably involving the coordination of the water molecules at the apices of a regular tetrahedron), and that the ions,[54] Mg^{2+}, as well as[55] Co^{2+}, and Ni^{2+}, in aqueous acetone solutions coordinate to six water molecules. The nuclear magnetic resonance technique depends on the fact that nuclei having a magnetic moment, such as the proton or the ^{17}O nucleus, often exhibit an NMR signal (corresponding to a transition among the nuclear energy levels) for each distinct chemical environment of the nucleus, *provided that* the rate of exchange of the nucleus among the environments is not rapid. For a system such as that represented by the equation

$$Be(^{17}OH_2)_4{}^{2+} + {}^{17}O\acute{H}_2 \rightleftharpoons Be(^{17}O\acute{H}_2)_4{}^{2+} + {}^{17}OH_2 \quad (4\text{–}28)$$

this would correspond to one distinct ^{17}O NMR signal for the four water molecules in the primary coordination sphere of Be^{2+} and one for water in the rest of the solution.*

These demonstrations of primary solvation force a consideration of three reasonable processes for the reaction of the OH^- ion with metal ions in solution (illustrated below for the specific case of Al(III)):

(1) Ion pairing which involves the association of the OH^- ion with the metal ion which retains its primary hydration sphere.

$$[Al(OH_2)_6]^{3+} + OH^- \rightleftharpoons \{[Al(OH_2)_6]^{3+}OH^-\} \quad (4\text{–}29)$$

(2) The conversion** of water to the OH^- ion.

$$[Al(OH_2)_6]^{3+} + OH^- \rightleftharpoons [Al(OH_2)_5OH]^{2+} + H_2O \quad (4\text{–}30)$$

(3) The conversion** of water to the OH^- ion accompanied by a decrease in the coordination number of the metal ion.

$$Al(OH_2)_6{}^{3+} + OH^- \rightleftharpoons [Al(OH_2)_3OH]^{2+} + 3\,H_2O \quad (4\text{–}31)$$

There is a precedent for each of these processes in the solution

[53] R. E. Connick and D. N. Fiat, *J. Chem. Phys.*, **39**, 1349 (1963).

[54] N. A. Matwiyoff and H. Taube, submitted for publication.

[55] N. A. Matwiyoff, submitted for publication.

** This does not require that all of the water molecules in the rest of the solution be in identical chemical environments (as they certainly should *not* be—some at any given instant must be closer to the $Be(OH_2)_4{}^{2+}$ ion than others) but rather that the rate of exchange of the water among the chemical sites outside the primary solvation sphere be rapid.

** It should be noted that these reactions actually may involve the abstraction of a proton from the primary coordination sphere of the metal ion.

chemistry of metal ions. Thus it has been found[56,57] that metal ions having well-defined primary coordination spheres, such as Co(III) in the $Co(NH_3)_6{}^{3+}$ ion, associate with a variety of anions, such as the $SO_4{}^{2-}$ ion, to form ion pairs such as $\{[Co(NH_3)_6]^{3+}SO_4{}^{2-}\}^+$. Replacement reactions are also quite common. For example, the slow reaction of the chloride ion with the $Cr(OH_2)_6{}^{3+}$ ion in aqueous solutions results in the formation of the $[CrCl(OH_2)_5]^{2+}$ ion. In contrast, the rapid reaction of $Fe(OH_2)_6{}^{3+}$ with concentrated aqueous HCl solutions to form the $FeCl_4{}^-$ ion involves a coordination number change at some stage in the replacement of water by Cl^- ion.[58,59]

It should be evident from this somewhat sketchy review that meaningful comparisons among the hydrolysis constants (and the appropriate ΔH^0 and ΔS^0 values) of metal ions can be drawn only if the structures of the aquo- and hydroxo-metal ion complexes in solution are known. For example, a quantitative comparison of the pK_h values of $Be^{2+}(aq)$ and $Al^{3+}(aq)$ would be meaningless unless explicit account is taken of the fact that the "polarizing power" of the Al^{3+} ion is distributed over six water molecules whereas that of the Be^{2+} ion is distributed over only four. The ambiguity also extends to the products of the reaction even in the event that reaction 4–31 can be excluded.* Does the hydroxo complex of Al(III) involve the coordination of four, $Al(OH_2)_3OH$, or six, $Al(OH_2)_5OH$, groups? In the light of the evaluation of ΔH^0 for hydrolysis from the temperature dependence of pK_h, another consideration arises. Are the primary hydration numbers temperature independent or is there a temperature

[56] F. Posey and H. Taube, *J. Am. Chem. Soc.*, **78**, 15 (1956).

[57] I. L. Jenkins and C. B. Monk, *J. Chem. Soc.*, 68 (1951).

[58] G. A. Gamlen and D. O. Jordan, *J. Chem. Soc.*, 1435 (1953).

[59] A. H. Zeltman and L. O. Morgan, *J. Phys. Chem.*, **70**, 2807 (1966).

* Many of the methods used to evaluate these equilibria depend on an evaluation of the activities of the species in solution and do *not* allow a distinction between ion pairs and complex ions. For example, conductivity studies under the proper conditions can be used to obtain the concentration of "free" ions in the solution. Unfortunately, it cannot distinguish the distribution of the ions which are not "free" into ion pairs (ions separated by one or more solvent molecules but which, nonetheless, act as a unit in executing vibrational, rotational, and translational motion in the solution) and complex ions: both would exhibit the same net charge to the electric field. A similar limitation applies to the measurement of the p*H* or p*OH* of the solution—the p*OH* is a measure of the activity of the "free" OH^- ion and does not distinguish the state of bonding of that which is not "free." For this reason there has been much interest in the so-called concentration methods for evaluating solution equilibria. In these methods, each species in a distinct chemical environment provides a response to a stimulus (*e.g.*, radiation) which is proportional to its concentration. Examples of concentration methods are NMR spectroscopy, discussed above, and the spectrophotometric analysis discussed in Chapter 3.

dependent equilibrium among species of different primary coordination numbers? In this context, it has been reported[60,61] that although $Co^{2+}(aq)$ exists almost exclusively as the octahedral ion, $Co(OH_2)_6{}^{2+}$, detectable amounts of the tetrahedral $Co(OH_2)_4{}^{2+}$ ion are present in the solution, particularly at elevated temperatures.

In view of the unanswered questions outlined above, meaningful comparisons of the data in Table 4–13 are not possible at present, but a great deal of progress in this important area can be expected in the near future. For a more complete discussion of these systems, the reader is directed to a recent introductory review by Hunt[62] and a more quantitative discussion by Monk.[63]

---

[60] T. J. Swift and R. E. Connick, *J. Chem. Phys.*, **37,** 307, (1962).

[61] T. J. Swift, *Inorg. Chem.*, **3,** 526, (1964).

[62] J. P. Hunt, *Metal Ions in Aqueous Solutions*, W. A. Benjamin, Inc., New York, 1963.

[63] C. B. Monk, *Electrolytic Dissociation*, Academic Press, Inc., New York, 1961, Chapter 14.

INDEX